Third Edition
Solutions

Upper-Intermediate

Workbook

Tim Falla **Paul A Davies**

Paul Kelly   Helen Wendholt   Sylvia Wheeldon

OXFORD

UNIVERSITY PRESS

OXFORD
UNIVERSITY PRESS

ACKNOWLEDGEMENTS

Alamy Stock Photo pp.4 (teen shopping/Agencja Fotograficzna Caro),
6 (doctor/MBI), 8 (elderly man/STOCKFOLIO®), 11 (Charlie Chaplin/Pictorial
Press Ltd), 14 (fans waving/OJO Images Ltd), 14 (celebrity and fans/OJO Images
Ltd), 20 (students talking/HA Photos), 22 (teens in library/Picture Partners),
31 (tourists at snack stand/PhotoStock-Israel), 36 (protesters/David Grossman),
36 (women's day poster/Bojan Mirkovic), 36 (city fireworks display/RooM the
Agency), 36 (New Years Eve poster/Laurel), 42 (whale watching/Kurt Lackovic),
46 (wake boarding/MARKA), 46 (paraglider/imageBROKER), 58 (parents and
son/ONOKY - Photononstop), 59 (teen comforting friend/Blend Images),
67 (edible worms/Marcin Rogozinski), 68 (teen and doctor/RGB Ventures/
SuperStock), 69 (teens exercising/Frank Paul), 77 (teen on phone/Jasminko
Ibrakovic), 101 (shopping mall/Kumar Sriskandan), 110 (Linkedin screen shot/
M4OS Photos), 112 (Great Dane/Arterra Picture Library), 116 (Gumtree screen
shot/M4OS Photos); Divine Chocolate p.117 (chocolate bars/Divine); Getty
Images pp.7 (teen in cafe/Bloom Productions), 10 (paparazzi/Caiaimage/Tom
Merton), 11 (Audrey Hepburn/Sunset Boulevard), 12 (boy and maths equation/
PeopleImages), 14 (boy band fans/MARTY MELVILLE), 18 (hikers/Education
Images), 21 (restaurant complaint/Image Source), 32 (business meeting/
Portra Images), 32 (group of friends/Compassionate Eye Foundation/Chris
Ryan), 33 (street performers/Emad Aljumah), 40 (hotel/Atlantide Phototravel),
43 (river and boat/CHAPUT Franck/hemispicture.com), 44 (George Orwell/
Popperfoto), 45 (swimming with crocodiles/Robert Cianflone), 45 (snake
massage/Uriel Sinai), 46 (gondola in Venice/Danita Delimont), 46 (boat trip
Venice/Alexander Haase/EyeEm), 53 (street performance/Anadolu Agency),
54 (two teens/Westend61), 57 (students studying/Jeff Greenough), 66 (woman
sleeping/Shuji Kobayashi), 74 (dancing at the beach/mihailomilovanovic),
75 (teen students/Jack Hollingsworth), 78 (UFO/Steven Peters), 79 (Orson
Welles/Popperfoto), 84 (brochure distribution/George Doyle), 85 (teen voting/
Philippe Lissac/GODONG), 86 (protesters/Matt Cardy), 88 (Rosa Parks/Universal
History Archive), 95 (woman using laptop/Petar Chernaev), 97 (littered beach/
Enrique Algarra), 100 (army soup kitchen/New York Times Co.), 102 (Chinese
restaurant/Glowimages), 102 (restaurant/Kathryn Barnard), 102 (Cotswolds
village/joe daniel price), 102 (Scotland landscape/Loop Images), 103 (teen
counting money/Daniel Sambraus), 108 (Jane Austen bank note/Bloomberg),
112 (bonnet ornament/Richard Cummins), 114 (online crime/Thomas
Trutschel); iStockphoto pp.45 (Petra/Hanis), 63 (antibiotics/unalozmen); Japan
National Tourism Organization p.41 (Japan hotel interior/Ryokan Hotel/
Japan National Tourism Organization); Lisa Hensel/Ben Moon collection
p.55 (man and dog/Lisa Hensel/Ben Moon collection); NASA p.113 (astronauts/
NASA); Oxford University Press pp.5 (parliament, Vienna/Photodisc),
19 (Manhattan/Photodisc), 73 (salad making/Paul Bradbury), 98 (euro notes/
Chris from Paris), 112 (terrier dog/naten), 116 (notice board/Photodisc);
Oxfam pp.87 (Oxfam logo/Oxfam), 87 (Oxfam providing water/Oxfam); Rex
Shutterstock pp.9 (Jennifer Lawrence/Stephen Lovekin/Variety), 14 (Lady Gaga/
Craig Borrow/Newspix), 24 (girls talking/Isopix), 25 (friends chatting/Cultura),
35 (The Kite Runner/Dreamworks), 56 (The Duff/Guy D'Alema/CBS Films/Vast
Entertainment/Wonderland Sound And Vision/Granville Pictures), 65 (Lee
Hadwin/Steve Meddle), 89 (The Help/Dreamworks Pictures), 96 (woman at
bookshop/Cultura), 108 (graduation ceremony/Caiaimage); Rosie Lee p.13 (girl
vlogging/Rosie Lee); Shutterstock pp.8 (horoscope signs/Tom K Photo),
34 (American flag/AXL), 37 (girl at bus stop/Kaesler Media), 45 (dangerous
walkway/flocu), 51 (family camping holiday/oliveromg), 51 (family holiday/
kurhan), 58 (parents arguing/threerocksimages), 58 (family argument/
Monkey Business Images), 62 (female brain/CLIPAREA l Custom media),
64 (woman running/l i g h t p o e t), 73 (chefs/Minerva Studio), 80 (security
camera/pixinoo), 107 (woman buying food/NatUlrich), 107 (clothes shopping/
luminast); Simon Rawles p.116 (farmers in Ghana/Simon Rawles).

Back cover photograph: Oxford University Press building/David Fisher

I Introduction

A Verb patterns
I can talk about friends and friendship.

1 Choose the correct verbs to complete the sentences.

1 Our teacher **wondered / insisted / encouraged** us to take part in the contest.
2 The student **blamed / denied / managed** taking the money from his classmate.
3 We all **reminded / persuaded / agreed** to meet in town at 8 p.m.
4 Did you **mention / spend / tell** the idea of going out for a pizza to Jessica?
5 Sean always **denies / offers / mentions** to help his friends.
6 If you **keep / expect / agree** trying, you will finally succeed!

2 Complete the sentences with the correct infinitive or -*ing* form of the verbs in brackets.

When I go shopping for clothes, I spend time ¹_____ (think) about what I'm going to buy. I usually can't afford ²_____ (buy) the brands I really like. If I spend all my money on one piece of clothing, I end up ³_____ (regret) it. However, if I really like something, I do occasionally decide ⁴_____ (do) that. I enjoy ⁵_____ (look) around the shops for cheaper clothes and I always ask the shop assistants ⁶_____ (give) me a discount. They usually refuse ⁷_____ (offer) me one, but occasionally I'm lucky and I manage ⁸_____ (get) one!

3 Match 1–6 with a–f to make sentences.

1 Kate always begs ☐
2 Jake blamed ☐
3 Anna suggested ☐
4 This ice cream reminds ☐
5 Tom won't ☐
6 Our neighbour didn't thank us ☐

a revising for the exams together.
b for finding his cat.
c his sister for their late arrival.
d mind waiting for us at the bus station.
e me to help her with her homework.
f me of our holiday in Italy.

4 Complete the sentences with the correct form of the verbs below.

accuse   apologise   beg   blame   insist   thank   want   warn

1 Amy and Ewan don't _____ to go to the concert.
2 Our parents _____ us against swimming in the river when we were on holiday.
3 Chloë _____ on using her mobile phone in the cinema even though she was asked not to.
4 Alex didn't _____ for arriving late.
5 We _____ them to take us on holiday.
6 Lucy always _____ other people for her problems.
7 I _____ Tom for helping me with my homework.
8 They _____ the students of lying.

5 Complete the sentences with *to do* or *doing*.

1 He admitted _____ badly in the exam.
2 Lucy has always enjoyed _____ exercise.
3 My dad persuaded me _____ the course.
4 The organisers thanked us for _____ the clearing up.
5 Mark insisted on _____ his homework alone.
6 Amy has promised _____ the washing-up.

6 Complete the text with the correct infinitive or -*ing* form of the verbs below. Sometimes both forms are correct.

be   fall   go   snow   spend   take   turn into

I prefer ¹_____ on holiday in the winter rather than in the summer, so I'll never forget ²_____ in the mountains on a skiing holiday last year. I was really excited when it started ³_____ during our first night at the hotel. However, the following morning, the snow hadn't stopped ⁴_____ . The coach from the hotel tried ⁵_____ us to the ski station, but the road was in a dangerous condition. The snow on the road had started ⁶_____ ice and we had to return to the hotel. I remember ⁷_____ my time looking out of the hotel window, hoping that they would clear the road!

7 Complete the sentences with the infinitive or -*ing* form of the verbs in brackets.

1 Our teacher first taught us some vocabulary and then went on _____ (explain) the meaning of the tenses.
2 Please remember _____ (take) your keys with you when you go out tonight.
3 Jack will always remember _____ (score) his first goal for the school football team.
4 We'll stop _____ (have) a break at 11 a.m. and then we'll return to working on the project.
5 We'll never forget _____ (meet) our favourite actor at the airport.
6 I'm afraid that I forgot _____ (buy) bread.

Grammar

Present and future tenses

I can use different tenses to talk about the present and future.

1 Choose the correct verbs to complete the sentences.

1 What **do you usually do / are you usually doing** at weekends?

2 Next time **I'm seeing / I see** Jenny, I'll tell her I've seen you.

3 **We're learning / We learn** about space travel at school this week.

4 What time **does the World Cup Final start / is the World Cup Final starting** tomorrow?

5 **Does your aunt work / Is your aunt working** in the centre of town?

6 My brother **is always using / always uses** my phone without asking. It's really annoying!

7 **Are you going / Do you go** to Ted's party on Saturday night?

2 Complete the sentences with *will* or *going to* and the verb in brackets.

1 Have you finished your tea? Pass me your cup and I _____ (pour) you some more.

2 Don't worry, we _____ (phone) you as soon as we reach the campsite.

3 If it's already half past six, we _____ (miss) the start of the film.

4 It doesn't matter if you don't have a jacket with you. I _____ (lend) you mine.

5 Max has worked hard, so I'm sure he _____ (do) well in the exam.

6 I've decided that next weekend I _____ (paint) my room a different colour.

3 Choose the correct answer (a or b) to complete the sentences.

1 Stefan is going camping
  a next week.   b every summer.

2 Have you decided what time
  a you're going out?   b you go out?

3 Tom is always talking
  a when the TV's on!   b clearly.

4 Can you give this to Ben next time
  a you're seeing him? b you see him?

5 I always
  a cycle to school.   b am cycling to school.

6 Do you play basketball
  a this Saturday?   b every Saturday?

4 Choose the correct verb (a–c) to complete the sentences.

1 'How often ___ running?' 'Twice a week, usually.'
  a are you going   b do you go   c will you go

2 'Is the café open today?' 'Yes, but it ___ at all on Sundays.'
  a isn't opening   b doesn't open   c won't open

3 Don't be late tomorrow – the bus ___ at nine o'clock.
  a will leave   b is going to leave   c leaves

4 Let's go for another swim after we ___ this drink.
  a are going to finish   b finish   c will finish

5 ___ anything interesting at the moment?
  a Are you reading   b Will you read   c Are you going to read

6 You look cold. I ___ you my hat to wear.
  a 'll give   b 'm giving   c 'm going to give

7 I'm so excited! My favourite singer ___ here in June.
  a plays   b will play   c is playing

8 Be careful! That ladder isn't safe – you ___ !
  a are falling   b are going to fall   c fall

5 Correct the underlined mistakes in the sentences. Use the correct present or future tense.

1 Una's favourite food is Chinese, but <u>I'm preferring</u> Mexican.
_____

2 The clouds in the distance are really black – <u>there will be</u> a storm. _____

3 The school term <u>is going to end</u> next Friday; I can't wait!
_____

4 Ellie <u>is practising</u> the guitar for an hour each day.
_____

5 The sun's just come out, so I think <u>I'm going</u> for a walk in the park. _____

6 When <u>you'll find out</u> the final score, let me know.
_____

7 My sister has decided that she <u>doesn't eat</u> chocolate until the end of this month. _____

8 Trains to London <u>will leave</u> here every half an hour.
_____

6 Complete the email with the correct form of the verbs in brackets. There may be more than one possible answer.

To: fred@email.com

Hi Fred!

How are you? I hope you ¹_____ (enjoy) the summer holidays. I haven't done much so far, but my aunt and uncle ²_____ (come) next week. They ³_____ (live) in Canada with my cousins, so I ⁴_____ (not see) them very often. They ⁵_____ (stay) with us for a fortnight, which is great! We plan to take them sightseeing as soon as they ⁶_____ (arrive). They haven't been here before, but I know they ⁷_____ (love) Austria. Let me know your news!

Florian

IC Vocabulary
Life events
I can talk about my family and life events.

1 Match the ages (a–g) with the stages of life (1–7).

1	be an adult	a	100+
2	be a centenarian	b	60+
3	be a toddler	c	13–19
4	be an infant	d	40–60
5	be elderly	e	1–3
6	be in your teens	f	0–1
7	be middle-aged	g	18+

2 Complete the sentences with the adjectives and prepositions below. You can use the prepositions more than once.

addicted   aware   curious   good   happy   obsessed
sensitive   shocked

about   at   by   of   to   with

1 Harry is _____ _____ money and he's always thinking of ways of making it.
2 We weren't _____ _____ the hotel, and nor were we pleased with the way the tour company handled the problem.
3 Don't say anything negative about her work because she's very _____ _____ criticism.
4 Children are _____ _____ everything around them and want to know how things work.
5 My grandparents would be offended by the language used on TV and _____ _____ the violence in films.
6 I'm not very _____ _____ maths and always get low marks in the exams.
7 She says she isn't _____ _____ chocolate, but I always see her eating it!
8 I didn't realise there was a problem, and I wasn't _____ _____ the risks.

3 Put the words below in the correct columns to form different life events.

a business   a family   divorced   engaged   home
married   school (x2)

get	leave	start

4 Choose the correct prepositions to complete the sentences.

1 My grandmother passed **over** / **through** / **away** at the age of 88.
2 Dan's parents split **up** / **off** / **in** when he was still a toddler.
3 Rachel was brought **on** / **at** / **up** by her aunt and uncle.
4 We grew **up** / **over** / **on** in a small village, and I loved living in the countryside.
5 Many people get married and settle **around** / **down** / **up** in their thirties.
6 My sister fell **to** / **on** / **in** love with a fellow student at university, and they became engaged a year later.

5 Replace the underlined words and phrases with the correct form of the words and phrases below.

emigrate   inherit   learn to drive   retire   settle down
split up

1 My dad is looking forward to <u>finishing work</u> next year and having more time for his hobbies. _____
2 When my grandad passed away, my mum <u>got</u> his house and some money. _____
3 My sister is <u>having driving lessons</u>. _____
4 My uncle and aunt <u>separated</u> last year after being married for fifteen years. _____
5 I don't want to <u>get married and have a family</u> until I've had a chance to see the world. _____
6 My older brother <u>moved to another country</u> last year to look for work. _____

6 Complete the sequences of events with the phrases below.

buy a house or flat   get divorced   get married
go to university   grow up   pass away

1 retire, become a grandparent, _____
2 fall in love, get engaged, _____
3 start school, leave school, _____
4 get married, split up, _____
5 be born, be brought up, _____
6 leave home, move house, _____

7 Complete the text with the correct form of the words below.

be   buy   career   fall   get   job   leave   married
settle   split   start   study

Not everybody does things in the same order. My uncle ¹_____ school at sixteen and got his first ²_____ a month later. Then he ³_____ a business and ⁴_____ engaged, and he got ⁵_____ at seventeen! When he was 25, he ⁶_____ up with his wife, sold his business and went back to school. Then he decided to ⁷_____ for a degree in medicine. At university, he ⁸_____ in love with another student, and my cousin ⁹_____ born a year after they left university. My uncle and aunt now work as doctors, and they have ¹⁰_____ a house and ¹¹_____ down near us. That's what I call changing your ¹²_____ – and your life!

Grammar

Past tenses

I can talk about events that took place in the past.

1 Complete the sentences with the past simple or past continuous form of the verb in brackets.

1 I _____ (have) a shower when the postman _____ (arrive).
2 Sandra _____ (drop) her bag while she _____ (run) for the bus.
3 He _____ (read) the letter when he suddenly _____ (start) to laugh.
4 The sun _____ (shine), so we _____ (decide) to have a barbecue.
5 She _____ (hurt) her finger while she _____ (cut) some bread.
6 Pat _____ (live) in Greece when he _____ (meet) Hannah.

2 Complete the sentences with the past simple or past perfect form of the verbs below.

arrive be complete decide finish get go lose
not know pass put start take tell

1 After we _____ eating, we _____ to go to the shops.
2 By the time they _____ at the theatre, the play _____ .
3 He only realised he _____ his keys when he _____ to his front door.
4 Jerry _____ delighted because he _____ all his exams.
5 When everyone _____ a chocolate, she _____ the box away.
6 They _____ out for a pizza after they _____ the project.
7 I _____ about the accident because no one _____ me about it.

3 Choose the correct verbs to complete the sentences.

1 My father **worked / has worked** as a policeman since he **left / has left** school.
2 Linda **called / has called** me this morning. She **has decided / decided** to come out with us later.
3 Tom **never drove / has never driven** a car because he's not old enough.
4 I **bought / have bought** a new shirt at the weekend, but I **didn't wear / haven't worn** it yet.
5 Pablo loves Sam Smith's new album, but I **haven't heard / didn't hear** it.
6 I **spilled / have spilled** water on my phone earlier; I think I **broke / I've broken** it.

4 Complete the dialogue with the present perfect simple or continuous form of the verbs in brackets.

Eve Hi, Will. ¹_____ (you finish) reading that magazine yet?
Will Not quite. I ²_____ (read) this article about Paris. It's really interesting.
Eve ³_____ (you visit) France, then?
Will Lots of times – we ⁴_____ (go) there on holiday for years. Recently, my aunt and uncle ⁵_____ (buy) a house there so we'll go even more often.
Eve Lucky you. I ⁶_____ (never visit) another country. Anyway, I ⁷_____ (make) a cake if you'd like a piece?
Will That's really kind, but no thanks. I ⁸_____ (eat) biscuits all morning and I'm full!

5 Choose the correct verbs (a–c) to complete the text.

Last night, I ¹__ to music when my phone ²__ ringing. It was my sister. She ³__ her bag and ⁴__ enough money to get a cab home. She ⁵__ to walk, but when it ⁶__ to rain, she ⁷__ to go to a café. She ⁸__ there and she wanted me to ask if Mum or Dad would drive over and pick her up!

1 a listened   b was listening   c had listened
2 a started   b had started   c was starting
3 a was losing   b lost   c had lost
4 a didn't have   b hadn't had   c wasn't having
5 a was starting   b started   c had started
6 a began   b had begun   c was beginning
7 a decided   b was deciding   c had decided
8 a had waited   b was waiting   c waited

6 Complete the sentences with the verbs in brackets. Use the correct past tense.

1 'Why is your face so red?' 'I _____ (sit) in the sun all morning.'
2 I _____ (try) to do this crossword all morning and I still can't finish it.
3 They were driving to the sea when the car _____ (run out) of petrol.
4 After they'd woken up, they _____ (cook) a big breakfast.
5 Rosa has eaten octopus, but she _____ (not try) snails before!
6 I _____ (guess) what was inside the parcel before I opened it.

1 Fame

Vocabulary

A What are they like?

I can describe people's personalities.

1 Choose the correct answers to complete the horoscopes.

Find out what is going to happen in your life with this week's horoscope!

 ARIES: You have been very ¹**industrious / eccentric** lately and all your hard work will finally pay off this week.

 TAURUS: You will have a bad experience on Wednesday, but a ²**cruel / sympathetic** friend will take care of you.

 GEMINI: Although you are normally ³**sociable / cautious**, this week you will take a risk that could change your life for the better!

 CANCER: Although you've been feeling ⁴**insecure / sympathetic** about your own abilities recently, news will arrive that will improve your confidence.

 LEO: Your ⁵**self-satisfied / outgoing** personality will make you lots of new friends who will enjoy your company at the weekend!

 VIRGO: Your ⁶**creative / untrustworthy** talent will help you express your artistic personality this week.

 LIBRA: You will receive news …

2 Put the adjectives below in the correct columns.

bad-tempered   bossy   considerate   creative   cruel
outgoing   quick-witted   selfless   self-satisfied
spontaneous   stingy   untrustworthy

Positive	Negative

3 🎧 1.02 Listen to four descriptions. Match the adjectives below with descriptions 1–4. There are two extra adjectives.

cruel   judgemental   spontaneous
stingy   stubborn   vain

Speaker 1 _____   Speaker 3 _____
Speaker 2 _____   Speaker 4 _____

4 🎧 1.02 Listen again and choose the correct answers (a–c).

1 The speaker thinks that Kevin is ___ .
  a untrustworthy   b bossy   c considerate
2 Olivia's behaviour suggests she could be ___ .
  a cruel   b cautious   c insecure
3 The speaker suggests that his grandmother is ___ .
  a judgemental   b sympathetic   c shrewd
4 When people disagree with Max, he becomes ___ .
  a bad-tempered   b cautious   c cruel

5 Replace the underlined words in the text with the adjectives below.

considerate   eccentric   passionate
pushy   quick-witted   shrewd

My grandfather can seem ¹a bit unusual in an amusing way at times _____ , but he says he just thinks differently. In fact, he's very ²good at understanding people and judging situations _____ and ³able to reply quickly to ideas that he doesn't agree with in a clever way _____ . Sometimes he can seem ⁴unpleasant when he really wants something _____ , but really, he's just ⁵showing his strong feelings about things that he likes _____ . However, when people get to know him, they all agree that he is a ⁶kind and helpful _____ man.

6 Complete the sentences with the words below.

hard   open   quick   self   thick   well

1 The students are always _____-behaved in their English class.
2 Amber isn't very _____-minded and she doesn't like trying new things.
3 Sean is usually quite _____-working, but he didn't study a lot for these exams.
4 He's _____-witted and he gave fast answers to the questions in the test.
5 You need to be _____-skinned to be a politician.
6 Max is _____-confident, but he knows talent is not enough to succeed.

7 Complete the sentences with compound adjectives.

1 We went to a restaurant with Andy last night and he was rude and unpleasant to everyone! He's always been b_____-m_____ .
2 You'd have to be very t_____-s_____ not to be upset by his insensitive remarks.
3 She devotes all her time to her training. She's very ambitious and s_____-m_____ when it comes to achieving her goals.
4 We saw a romantic comedy at the theatre last weekend which was fun and quite l_____-h_____ .
5 Lily was very s_____-c_____ before the exam because she'd studied a lot and knew she would do well.
6 I've met quite a few relaxed people in my life, but I've never known anyone as e_____-g_____ as Mark.

Grammar

Past perfect simple and past perfect continuous

I can use the past perfect simple and past perfect continuous.

1 Complete the sentences with the past perfect simple form of the verbs in brackets.

1 He made a dentist's appointment because he _____ (break) a tooth.

2 We _____ (not leave) enough time, so we missed our train.

3 After she _____ (choose) a new skirt, she looked for a top to match it.

4 I couldn't make my new tablet work because I _____ (lose) the instructions.

5 When I checked the receipt later, I realised I _____ (pay) too much for my shopping.

6 Sam forgot to take a hat on the camping trip, but luckily his friend _____ (bring) a spare one.

7 The car went off the road because it _____ (hit) a patch of ice.

8 You would have saved money if you _____ (buy) that DVD in the sale.

2 Complete the sentences with the past perfect continuous form of the verbs below.

cook   hurt   learn   look   travel   try   wait   work

1 We _____ for less than an hour when the coach broke down.

2 I _____ for my friend for an hour when he phoned to say he couldn't come.

3 When I met Dean, he _____ as a teacher in Argentina since 2012.

4 I could tell my mum _____ because the kitchen smelled of curry.

5 They _____ for their dog for two days when it turned up outside their house.

6 My cousin _____ to drive for over a year before she passed her test.

7 He eventually went to the doctor because his leg _____ for a week.

8 I _____ to get a ticket to the show for several minutes when the website crashed.

3 Write the words in the correct order to make sentences.

1 you / went / eaten / Had / you / breakfast / out / before / ?
_____

2 long / They / bus / waiting / the / hadn't / arrived / been / when _____

3 been / swimming / because / just / was / He / cold / he'd _____

4 before / London / he / living / to / Where / he / had / been / moved / ? _____

5 so / expected / presents / get / hadn't / She / to / many _____

6 before / for / long / married / they / dating / they / Had / been / got / ? _____

4 Complete the sentences with the words in brackets. Use the past perfect simple or past perfect continuous.

1 I (never / snorkel) before Mia took me last year.
_____

2 Clara was annoyed because the book she'd ordered (not / arrive).
_____

3 How long (you / play) the guitar before we met?
_____

4 By the time the shops opened, (they / queue) for nearly an hour.
_____

5 I looked for my bag, but (I forgot) where I'd put it.
_____

6 Greg was tired last night because (he / play) basketball.
_____

5 Complete the text with the past perfect simple or past perfect continuous form of the verbs below.

date   enjoy   find   not imagine   live   star   think

Jennifer Lawrence was born in the United States in 1990. Once, before she became famous, she ¹_____ about being a doctor and ²_____ that she'd ever become an actress. That changed when she was fourteen. She ³_____ a spring break with her parents when a stranger spotted her and asked to do a screen test. Then things progressed fast. Not long after she ⁴_____ work in commercials for MTV, she appeared in a TV series. Her family ⁵_____ in Kentucky for many years, but they moved to Los Angeles when her career took off. Two years before filming *The Hunger Games* in 2012, she ⁶_____ in *Winter's Bone* and been nominated for an Oscar. She ⁷_____ Nicholas Hoult, her co-star from *X-Men*, for two years when they split up in 2013.

6 Complete the second sentence with a past perfect tense so that it means the same as the first.

1 It was months since he'd played tennis.
He _____ for months.

2 She ate her dinner and then went to bed.
After she _____, she went to bed.

3 Zoe saved for ages and then bought a new watch.
Zoe _____ before she bought a new watch.

4 Eric broke his arm so he couldn't go to school.
Eric couldn't go to school _____.

5 We sat in the park for an hour and then it got dark.
By the time it _____ in the park for an hour.

6 It was his first visit to Europe.
He _____ Europe before.

Press intrusion
I can identify the attitude of a speaker.

Revision: Student's Book page 11

1 Complete the text with the words below.

harassed   interest   investigative   journalists   laws
libel   paparazzi   scandal   tabloid

The pop star invited ¹_____ from several
newspapers to discuss the stories about him in the
²_____ press. The star denied taking drugs and
sued the papers for ³_____ . He also complained
of being repeatedly ⁴_____ by the
⁵_____ outside his house since publication of
the stories. Furthermore, he said that privacy
⁶_____ needed to be strengthened for all
celebrities. However, the judge ruled that the tabloid's
story was ⁷_____ journalism rather than just a
celebrity ⁸_____ , and therefore it was in the
public ⁹_____ .

Listening Strategy

When you listen, pay attention to what words each
speaker uses to express his/her attitude. Words with a
similar meaning may have different connotations.

**2 🎧 1.03 Read the Listening Strategy. Then listen to five
dialogues and choose the word the second speaker uses.**

1 The second speaker describes the new person she met as
   shy / bad-mannered.
2 The second speaker says that the singer's costume was
   creative / colourful.
3 The second speaker describes the footballer as being
   shrewd / judgemental.
4 The second speaker thinks the politician is **open-minded /
   single-minded.**
5 The second speaker says that newspapers offer us
   propaganda / information.

**3 🎧 1.03 For each speaker, choose the correct attitude (a–c).
Use your answers to exercise 2 to help you. Listen again
and check.**

1 The second speaker was ___ when she met her friend's new
   partner.
   a unimpressed   **b** bored   **c** enthusiastic
2 The second speaker ___ the singer's outfit.
   a disapproves of   **b** disbelieves   **c** admires
3 The second speaker is ___ when talking about the footballer.
   a disapproving   **b** unimpressed   **c** uninterested
4 The second speaker is ___ in her attitude to the politician.
   a critical   **b** approving   **c** disbelieving
5 The second speaker is ___ with tabloid news.
   a disappointed   **b** surprised   **c** impressed

**4 Say these lines from the dialogues. Try to express the
attitude in brackets.**

1 Hey, did you enjoy the party? Who was there? Tell me all
   about it! (enthusiastic)
2 Did you see the outfit that Rihanna was wearing at the
   Music Awards? Rather bright, wasn't it? (critical)
3 I wish that footballer would keep his views to himself.
   He's always got too much to say about the other players.
   (annoyed)
4 The Education Minister is now saying that teachers deserve
   a pay rise. That's a complete change of opinion! (surprised)
5 I'm so tired of the tabloid news. It's very one-sided. (weary)

**5 🎧 1.04 Listen and match speakers 1–4 with sentences A–E.
There is one extra sentence.**

A The speaker is angry about the lack of accuracy in news
   reporting. ☐
B The speaker is critical of people's lack of interest in
   improving society. ☐
C The speaker admits to an interest in celebrity gossip. ☐
D The speaker feels that news about celebrities is
   unrealistic. ☐
E The speaker feels that news reporting is pessimistic. ☐

1D Grammar
used to and *would*
I can correctly use used to and would.

1 Complete each sentence with the correct form of *used to* and the verbs below.

be   be   have   not have   not use   not want

1 She _____ married, but she isn't married any more.
2 He _____ short hair, but now it's really short!
3 In the past, people _____ social media, but now they use it all the time.
4 'You _____ a motorbike, did you?' 'No, but I want one now.'
5 My favourite actor _____ a moustache, but he shaved it off.
6 I'm not scared of spiders, but I _____ when I was younger.

2 Choose the correct answers (a or b) to complete the text.

BEFORE THEY BECAME FAMOUS

Before they became famous, many celebrities ¹___ have the superstar lifestyles we associate with them today. Glamorous actress and three-time Oscar nominee Amy Adams ²___ as a waitress when she was eighteen. And when Brad Pitt was employed by restaurant chain El Pollo Loco, he ³___ to dress as a chicken and wave at passing cars. Rapper and fashion icon Kanye West ⁴___ own such chic outfits when he worked for Gap, folding clothes. And Barack Obama ⁵___ one summer serving ice cream in Honolulu, Hawaii. Apparently the ice cream was so hard that it ⁶___ make his wrists hurt, and he confesses that, of course, he ⁷___ eat too much ice cream, so he doesn't like it any more!

1 **a** wouldn't	**b** didn't use to
2 **a** would work	**b** used to work
3 **a** used	**b** would
4 **a** didn't use to	**b** wouldn't
5 **a** spent	**b** used to spend
6 **a** wouldn't	**b** used to
7 **a** would	**b** used to

3 Complete the second sentence with *used to* so that it means the same as the first.

1 Ten years ago, this shopping centre wasn't here.
Ten years ago, this shopping centre didn't _____ here.
2 I thought he once lived in New York.
Didn't _____ in New York?
3 When I was learning to play chess, I lost a lot of games.
I _____ when I was learning to play chess.
4 Originally, he wanted to be a professional footballer.
_____ to be a professional footballer.
5 Wasn't she a waitress in the past?
Didn't _____ a waitress?
6 He's only had a sports car since he became famous.
Before he became famous, he _____ a sports car.

4 Complete the text with *used to* or *would* and the verbs in brackets. Sometimes both are possible.

In the past, people ¹_____ (find) fame by being an actor, a sports star, a singer and so on. And even very talented people ²_____ (know) that they'd only get a 'big break' by achieving something really special that brought them to the public's attention. Before the rise of social media, people ³_____ (not become) famous just for being famous. There ⁴_____ (not be) celebrities like Justin Bieber, who rose to fame after posting videos of himself online. But there's a downside – perhaps careers ⁵_____ (not rise) so fast, but they also ⁶_____ (not crash) so spectacularly; nowadays a damaging story or photo can go viral on the internet in minutes. And in the past, the famous at least had some privacy and ⁷_____ (not need) to be available to their fans on Twitter 24/7!

5 Complete the sentences with *used to* or *would* and the correct form of the verbs below. There may be more than one possible answer.

bite   eat   know   make   not think   visit

1 I _____ a lot of meat, but I prefer vegetarian food now.
2 We _____ my grandparents every week when I was a child.
3 Eva _____ about travelling the world until she went to Holland last year.
4 She _____ her fingernails, but she grew out of it.
5 My aunt _____ her own clothes when she was a student.
6 I _____ how to speak French, but I've forgotten now.

6 Correct the underlined mistakes in the sentences. Only use the past simple when it is the only correct answer.

1 Most of us <u>would believe</u> in Santa Claus when we were younger. _____
2 People <u>wouldn't be</u> so obsessed with celebrities before the internet. _____
3 <u>Would you use to</u> enjoy eating vegetables as a child?
_____
4 He <u>would study</u> engineering for two years before he became an actor. _____
5 My sister <u>would hate</u> having her hair cut when she was little. _____
6 <u>Would</u> famous actors use to earn so much money in the past? _____

Position and order of adjectives

I can use adjectives correctly.

1 Choose the correct answers (a–c) to complete the sentences.

1 On our trip, we visited a shop selling ___ furniture.
   a old beautiful Chinese   b Chinese beautiful old
   c beautiful old Chinese

2 We ordered some ___ olives with our meal.
   a small black Greek   b Greek black small
   c black small Greek

3 My parents are buying a ___ sofa next week.
   a new red comfortable   b red comfortable new
   c comfortable new red

4 Our favourite singer has just married a ___ politician.
   a middle-aged German tall   b tall middle-aged German
   c German tall middle-aged

5 In the story, a girl finds the key to a ___ box.
   a strange black antique   b black strange antique
   c strange antique black

6 Look at those ___ kittens – they're so cute!
   a white young tiny   b tiny young white
   c young tiny white

2 Choose the correct answers (a or b) to complete the text.

A young contestant at the Mental Calculation World Cup

There are more and more reports of child prodigies – children with exceptional talents. One of these is the ¹___ maths genius Cameron Thompson. As a ²___ boy, he corrected his teacher by saying that zero isn't the lowest number, because she had forgotten about negative numbers. A(n) ³___ girl called Priyanshi Somani won the Mental Calculation World Cup in 2010, held at the relatively ⁴___ university of Magdeburg. And a ⁵___ boy from Berlin started playing the violin at the age of two. Akim Camara has performed in front of 18,000 people, wearing a ⁶___ suit and playing a baby-size violin.

1 a Welsh amazing   b amazing Welsh
2 a clever four-year-old b four-year-old clever
3 a Indian young   b young Indian
4 a new German   b German new
5 a remarkable little   b little remarkable
6 a black tiny   b tiny black

3 Complete each sentence with the most appropriate two adjectives below in the correct order.

ancient delicious famous Greek Italian purple
tiny Turkish white young

1 The red and _____ flag has a moon and a star on it.
2 The Parthenon is a(n) _____ temple in Athens.
3 She picked up the _____ boy to stop him from crying.
4 Michelangelo was a(n) _____ painter.
5 Let's make a fruit salad – we can use these _____ grapes.

VOCAB BOOST!

Adjectives which are only used after a linking verb (*appear, become, feel,* etc.) often describe feelings or begin with '*a*' (*asleep, alive, alone,* etc.). Your dictionary should tell you if an adjective cannot go before a noun.

afraid /əˈfreɪd/ *adj.* [not before noun]
1 feeling fear; frightened because you think that you might be hurt or suffer: *Don't be afraid.* ◆ ~ **of sb/sth** *It's all over. There's nothing to be afraid of now.* ◆ *Are you afraid of spiders?*

4 Read the *Vocab boost!* box and the dictionary entry. Choose the correct adjective. If both are correct, put a tick.

1 Don't be **afraid / frightened**; the dog won't hurt you. ☐
2 His only **alive / living** relatives live in New Zealand. ☐
3 Are you **angry / annoyed** because I'm late? ☐
4 It's **a lonely / an alone** life on that tiny island. ☐
5 The **glad / happy** students celebrated the end of their exams with a party. ☐
6 Shut the door quietly – your father's **asleep / sleeping**. ☐

5 Complete the sentences with the words below. Use a dictionary to help you.

alone asleep aware content cross irritable
sorry sure

1 I can't be _____ , but that looks like Jaime over there.
2 If your brother's still _____ , he's going to miss breakfast!
3 When I'm on holiday, I always feel _____ just to sit on the beach and sunbathe.
4 No one was _____ that the date of the test had been changed.
5 Does your sister live _____ or with friends?
6 She seems really _____ about the accident.
7 He becomes _____ when he hasn't had enough sleep.
8 Emma looks really _____ . What did you say to make her so angry?

Vloggers

I can understand an article about vloggers.

Revision: Student's Book page 14

1 Complete the sentences with the words below.

accessibility channel content feedback interaction
platforms provider subscribers

1 Have you had any _____ from users about what they think of the new site?
2 There's not enough communication or _____ between the vlogger and his followers.
3 _____ to our blogs get regular updates every day.
4 Hopefully the new network will improve _____ to the internet in our neighbourhood.
5 His ideas are available on a number of media _____ including the internet and traditional newspapers.
6 Sam has set up his own _____ on YouTube and will start uploading videos soon.
7 His videos are very well made, but they need more original _____ to attract viewers.
8 The website is the largest _____ of Hollywood films for rent.

2 Read the text. What qualities do people who want to start a blog or vlog need?

Reading Strategy
Read the multiple-choice questions and all possible answers carefully. Find the part of the text that each question refers to. Read the answers again and choose the one that best matches the information in the text. Check that the other answers are incorrect.

3 Read the Reading Strategy. Then read the text again and choose the correct answers (a–d).

1 Kate Ross's job involves explaining to companies
   a how they can employ bloggers and vloggers.
   b what bloggers and vloggers do.
   c how they can collaborate with bloggers and vloggers.
   d which bloggers and vloggers earn the most money.
2 If you want your blog or vlog to be successful, you need
   a to write about passionate topics.
   b to really want to earn money.
   c to be interested in your viewers.
   d material that will catch people's attention.
3 If you want advertisers to notice you, you need to
   a have lots of viewers.
   b work for free.
   c be well organised.
   d talk about fashion.
4 The way the media presents the success that young bloggers and vloggers have had is
   a mistaken.   c enthusiastic.
   b accurate.   d positive.

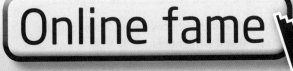

Online fame

ASK ROSIE

Surely blogging or vlogging must be one of the easiest ways of finding fame and fortune? All you need is a computer and a hobby to talk about, don't you? Well, although it looks simple, being a success in the blogosphere is actually a lot more difficult than it seems.

Kate Ross has been advising brands on how to work with bloggers and vloggers, and believes that if you start a blog or vlog just to earn money, it isn't going to work. Kate says you need to be passionate about your topic and you need to provide your readers or viewers with interesting content. If you don't, your vlog or blog isn't going to get positive feedback and attract subscribers.

You also need to be aware that cash isn't going to come rolling in overnight. Seventeen-year-old Rosie Bea, who has a YouTube fashion channel, says her blog only started attracting the attention of advertisers after she had put in months and months of unpaid work and built up a big fan base. Rosie was also combining her vlog work with her law studies, and she advises vloggers in the same position to make sure that they plan carefully so that they have time to do both things properly.

So, while the tabloid press often talks about the instant success of young bloggers and vloggers, it isn't really instant at all. The people who are successful have done well because they are hard-working and passionate about what they do, and it is this dedication and passion that attracts subscribers and advertisers to them. The press is only interested in them once they are in the public eye, but they have achieved their celebrity status through hours and hours of hard work.

1G Speaking

Photo comparison

I can compare photos and give opinions about fame.

1 Complete the sentences about photo A with the words below.

looks   most likely   say   something   sort of   sure

1 I can't be _____ , but I don't think that it's a concert.
2 It _____ like they're in the open air.
3 There's a _____ railing in front of the fans.
4 The group could be arriving at an airport, or _____ like that.
5 The fans in front are _____ friends as well, because it seems they have made a banner together.
6 I'd _____ that they were excited about seeing their favourite band.

2 Match the gaps in sentences 1–5 with the word and phrases below (a–f).

1 In both photos, you can see ___ .
2 The common theme in the photos is ___ .
3 The main difference between the photos is that ___ .
4 In the first photo ___ , whereas in the second photo ___ .
5 Unlike the second photo, the first photo shows ___ .

a the celebrity must be there in the second photo
b fame and celebrities
c they're screaming and shouting
d the fans holding a large banner
e the fans are waiting for the celebrities to arrive
f a group of fans

> **Speaking Strategy**
> When you talk about a photo, try to use a range of adjectives. For example, extreme adjectives can make your description more expressive.

> Compare the photos. Then give your opinion about why fans get so excited about seeing their favourite celebrities. Describe a concert or a show that you've been to recently.

3 🎧 1.05 Read the Speaking Strategy and the task above. Then listen to a student doing the task. Which four of the extreme adjectives below does she use? Match them with adverbs 1–4.

awful   delighted   ecstatic   exhausted   fascinated   hilarious   miserable   starving   terrible   terrified   thrilled   wonderful

1 absolutely _____
2 really _____
3 completely _____
4 totally _____

4 🎧 1.05 Listen again. Which two of the points (a–c) does the student mention in answer to the question in the task?

a They find their favourite celebrities very attractive. ☐
b The celebrities seem unreal until they see them in real life. ☐
c They get more excited because they're in a group. ☐

5 Look at the task and the photos below. Then read the questions (1–4) and write notes.

> Compare the photos. Then give your own opinion about whether celebrities should spend more time with their fans.

1 What is the common theme of the photos?
_____

2 What can you see in both photos?
_____

3 What is the main difference between the photos?
_____

4 Do you think celebrities should spend more time with their fans? Why? / Why not?
_____
_____

6 Now do the task using your notes from exercise 5.

1H Writing

A formal letter

I can write a formal letter.

Preparation

1 Read the task and the letter below. In which paragraph (A–D) does the writer ...

1 conclude the letter? ___
2 state the reason for writing? ___
3 make suggestions? ___
4 explain the reason for requesting the charity's presence? ___

> You are helping to organise a charity week for your school. You want to invite someone who will give an inspiring talk to the students. Write a letter to the president of a local charity organisation, and suggest what topics the talk should cover.

Dear Sir or Madam

A I am writing to invite you or one of your members to speak to students during our school charity week.

B Our school is organising a week next term when all the students will do something for charity. We would like to raise as much money as possible. I wonder whether someone from your organisation would ¹consider making a speech to the school on this topic? ²In my view, it would really ³benefit us all to have someone inspire us before we take on this challenge.

C I am sure you have your own thoughts on what it would be useful to cover. However, in addition to your own ideas, I would ⁴recommend including some advice on how to organise ourselves efficiently. In addition, it would be interesting to know which particular activities and events might be the most successful for raising money. Furthermore, we would appreciate some information on the best ways to advertise what we are doing. Finally, perhaps you could talk to us about the work of your charity. It would be inspiring to hear about how your organisation has ⁵contributed to society and made a difference to people's lives.

D I hope you will consider my request to talk at our school about raising money for charity. ⁶I look forward to hearing from you ⁷at your earliest convenience.

Yours faithfully

Chris Adams, Year 13

2 Read the Writing Strategy. Match the underlined formal expressions in the letter with the informal ones below.

as soon as possible   be good for   I can't wait to hear   given   suggest   I think   think about talking

3 Match the underlined informal parts of sentences 1–8 with formal phrases a–h.

1 I am writing to give you my ideas on our project. ☐
2 Our school recycling week is happening next month. ☐
3 I want to tell you which topics should be covered. ☐
4 My reasons are these. ☐
5 I hope you like my ideas. ☐
6 I think a talk from you would be very motivating. ☐
7 I'd like it if you would consider my request. ☐
8 Please write back soon. ☐

a as follows
b consider my recommendations favourably
c takes place
d put forward
e I look forward to hearing from you
f would like to suggest
g I would be grateful
h In my view,

Writing Guide

4 Read the task. Then plan your letter.

> You are on a committee to organise a careers advice week for your school. You want to invite someone who will give an inspiring talk about the world of work. Write a letter to the manager of the local employment centre, inviting him/her and suggesting useful topics to cover.

1 Why would you like someone to come and talk?
_____
_____

2 Why will it be beneficial for the school and students?
_____
_____

3 What topics would you like to hear about?
_____
_____

5 Write your letter.

CHECK YOUR WORK
👁 **Have you ...**
☐ followed your paragraph plan?
☐ started and finished the letter appropriately?
☐ avoided contractions and informal language?

Review Unit 1

Vocabulary

1 Choose the correct answers (a–c) to complete the sentences.

1 My aunt's rather ___ . She wears very weird clothes.
  a cautious   b eccentric   c industrious
2 Thanks for waiting. It was really ___ of you.
  a stingy   b passionate   c considerate
3 Mark's quite a ___ businessman. He tends to make good decisions.
  a critical   b selfless   c shrewd
4 Patricia's so ___ ! She's always looking at herself in the mirror.
  a vain   b cruel   c affectionate
5 My friends weren't very ___ when my budgie died. They just laughed!
  a bossy   b sympathetic   c outgoing
6 You're so ___ ! I wish you were a bit more flexible.
  a stubborn   b spontaneous   c creative

Mark: / 6

2 Complete the sentences with compound adjectives formed from the words below.

behave   go   mind   skin   temper   work

1 Nobody in my family likes visiting my grandfather. He's really _____ .
2 I'm quite _____ , so I don't usually get upset if people are rude to me.
3 Those children are very _____ . They do exactly what they're told.
4 My parents never judge people. They're really _____ .
5 She studies for four hours every night. She's very _____ .
6 Nothing seems to bother my best friend. She's very _____ .

Mark: / 6

3 Complete the sentences with a suitable media word.

1 The paparazzi are always invading people's _____ .
2 The singer sued the newspaper for _____ after the article it published about her.
3 Press _____ are in charge of what can and cannot be reported in the news.
4 Investigative _____ has led to a number of political scandals being revealed recently.
5 Celebrities are always in the public _____ .
6 Privacy _____ prevented the identity of the victim from being released.

Mark: / 6

Word Skills

4 Choose the correct adjective to complete the sentences.

1 The **afraid / frightened** children hid during the storm.
2 We heard **angry / annoyed** voices from next door.
3 There are a lot of **alone / lonely** old people in the world.
4 There were a lot of **glad / happy** faces at the party.
5 He picked up the **asleep / sleeping** child and put her to bed.

Mark: / 5

5 Choose the correct words to complete the sentences.

1 The music streaming service Spotify has over 20 million **providers / subscribers** worldwide.
2 One of the funniest things about the show is the **channel / interaction** between the comedian and the audience.
3 Which **provider / subscriber** offers the best service?
4 The **content / platform** on the website isn't good.
5 Does internet **accessibility / feedback** decrease the further you move away from your router?

Mark: / 5

6 Replace the underlined words with extreme adjectives.

1 That film was <u>very funny</u>. _____
2 We were <u>very tired</u> when we got home because we'd been travelling all day. _____
3 My sister was <u>really angry</u> when I spilled coffee on her laptop. _____
4 I'm <u>really hungry</u> because I didn't have time for breakfast this morning. _____
5 The little boy couldn't take his eyes off the magic show. He was <u>really interested</u>. _____
6 The actress was <u>very frightened</u> when she heard that someone was stalking her. _____

Mark: / 6

7 Complete the sentences with the phrases below.

be sure   looks like   most likely   say that   some kind

1 They're _____ journalists, or something like that.
2 It looks to me like a festival of _____ .
3 I can't _____ , but I think it's Broadway.
4 I'd _____ she was enjoying all the publicity.
5 It _____ some kind of castle, or maybe a palace.

Mark: / 5

Grammar

8 Complete the text with the past perfect simple or past perfect continuous form of the verbs in brackets.

Producers Neil Meron and Craig Zaidan [1]_____ (make) films for years before they took over the organisation of the Oscars ceremony in 2012. In fact, they [2]_____ (win) an Academy award themselves – for the musical *Chicago*. Once they [3]_____ (accept) the job, they set about giving the event a facelift. They felt that the winners [4]_____ (take) too long to get to the microphone in recent years, which meant that the ceremony [5]_____ (become) tedious. They changed the seating arrangements and they also tried to make the show more entertaining. A good example of this was with a mid-show pizza delivery during the 2014 ceremony. Meron and Zaiden [6]_____ (worry) about this moment since the host [7]_____ (suggest) it to them. They were relieved when it was over as they [8]_____ (not tell) the delivery boy he would be on the Oscars, so they didn't know how he would react.

Mark: ____ / 8

9 Choose the correct words to complete the dialogue. Sometimes both answers are correct.

Girl   Tell me about your best friend at school.

Mum   There was a girl called Jo. She [1]**lived / would live** across the road from me and we [2]**were / used to be** best friends for about five years.

Girl   [3]**Did you use to go / Would you go** to the same school?

Mum   Yes, but she was a year younger than me, so we [4]**didn't use to hang out / wouldn't hang out** together at school. But we [5]**used to see / would see** each other every weekend.

Girl   What [6]**did you use to do / would you do**?

Mum   Oh, the usual things like listening to music. But when Eurovision was on, we [7]**used to watch / would watch** the show together. That's what I remember most about her.

Mark: ____ / 7

Use of English

10 Complete the second sentence so that it means the same as the first. Write up to five words, including the word in brackets.

1   My parents don't trust us. (are)
    My parents think we _____ people.

2   My younger sister doesn't deny that she only has her studies on her mind – nothing distracts her from her goals. (is)
    My younger sister admits that she _____ when it comes to her studies – nothing distracts her from her goals.

3   I last saw Anna when we were at school, so I hardly recognised her. (hadn't)
    I hardly recognised Anna because I _____ we were at school.

4   He started singing many years before he got a recording contract. (had)
    He only got a recording contract after he _____ many years.

5   It was a habit of mine to bite my nails when I was a child. (used)
    As a child, _____ my nails.

6   In the past, people weren't so keen on becoming famous. (didn't)
    People _____ so keen on becoming famous.

Mark: ____ / 6

Total: ____ / 60

I can ...

Read the statements. Think about your progress and tick one of the boxes.

★ = I need more practice.   ★★★ = No problem!

★★ = I sometimes find this difficult.

	★	★★	★★★
I can describe people's personalities.			
I can use the past perfect simple and past perfect continuous.			
I can identify the attitude of a speaker.			
I can correctly use *used to* and *would*.			
I can use adjectives correctly.			
I can understand an article about vloggers.			
I can compare photos and give opinions about fame.			
I can write a formal letter.			

2 Problems

A It drives me crazy!
I can describe feelings and emotions.

1 Match the adjectives below with the sentences.

amused   ashamed   content   envious   furious   stunned

1 'I'd prefer not to talk about it. I'm still in a state of shock.'

_____

2 'That was really funny! I couldn't stop laughing!'

_____

3 'I've never been treated like this before! I shall be speaking to the manager!' _____

4 'Anybody could have done it. She was just lucky!'

_____

5 'We were very pleased with our presentation.'

_____

6 'How could I have forgotten her name? I feel so embarrassed about it!' _____

2 Replace the underlined adjectives with the adjectives below.

disappointed   indecisive   miserable   thrilled   upbeat

We were ¹really excited _____ when the storm started, but the longer it went on, the more anxious we became. We felt ²very unsure _____ and didn't know what to do. Should we stay under the trees or run for home?

Jack was quite ³positive _____ about the news that we were going to have a new trainer, but the rest of us were ⁴really sad _____ . But when we were told that the new trainer was inexperienced, even Jack felt ⁵let down _____ !

3 Choose the correct adjectives to complete the sentences.

1 We felt **upbeat / humiliated** after losing the match against our biggest rivals 10–0!

2 My mum says she feels **frustrated / anxious** in her job because she can't achieve what she wants.

3 I was **irritated / thrilled** by Sara's constant questions about my private life.

4 There was a positive, **furious / upbeat** feeling after the head teacher's speech.

5 Amy is **envious / disillusioned** of my new coat and she wishes that she had bought it first!

6 Harry has bad memories of his childhood and he is very **hysterical / bitter** about it.

4 Match the adjectives with the definitions.

bitter   disappointed   disillusioned   exasperated   hysterical   stressed

1 Feeling irritated and angry about a situation that you can't do anything about. _____

2 Unhappy because something or someone wasn't as good as you expected. _____

3 Feeling extremely worried and nervous about something, especially something you are expected to do. _____

4 Unable to control your feelings because of extreme fear or excitement. _____

5 Feeling unhappy because you discover the truth about someone or something. _____

6 Feeling or showing anger, hurt or resentment because of bad experiences or treatment. _____

5 Match 1–9 with a–i to form idioms.

1 lose		a	your top
2 blow		b	two minds about something
3 be on		c	on your nerves
4 be green		d	your hair out
5 be down		e	face
6 be in		f	edge
7 be over		g	with envy
8 be tearing		h	in the dumps
9 something gets		i	the moon

6 🎧 1.06 Listen to four dialogues. Complete the sentences with an idiom from exercise 5.

1 Jack says he _____ about going to Sam's party.

2 Ann says she _____ about her exam results.

3 The boy says that Meg's complaining _____ .

4 Ewan _____ about not getting the summer job.

7 🎧 1.06 Listen again and choose the correct answers (a–c).

1 If Jack doesn't go to Sam's party, Jack will ___ .
   a blow his top   b tear his hair out
   c lose face

2 When Kate hears about Ann's results, she will ___ .
   a be on edge   b be over the moon
   c be green with envy

3 The girl thinks that Meg ___ over unimportant things.
   a tears her hair out   b is over the moon
   c blows her top

4 The boy says that Ewan was ___ about the interview he was going to.
   a losing face   b on edge
   c tearing his hair out

2B Grammar
Comparison
I can make comparisons.

1 Complete the sentences with the comparative or superlative form of the adverb in brackets.

1 Who works _____ (hard) out of all the students in the class?

2 There isn't much traffic today, so we should arrive _____ (soon) than we expected.

3 If you ate _____ (slowly), you'd enjoy your food more!

4 The Swiss tennis player performed _____ (well) than his opponent and won the tournament.

5 Erik did _____ (badly) than I did in this month's test.

6 The world's population is growing _____ (fast) today than at any point in history.

7 My grandparents' house isn't far, but my aunt lives _____ (near) of all my family.

2 Match the two halves of the comparative sentences.

1 He's far more handsome in real life
2 The harder you work,
3 I spent more this week
4 The later you leave tonight,
5 The sooner we book,
6 This ice cream is less tasty
7 Our cat's getting bigger and bigger

a the colder it will be.
b than I'd wanted to.
c the cheaper the tickets will be.
d than on TV.
e than it looks.
f the more we feed it!
g the better you'll do.

3 Write the words in the correct order to make comparative sentences.

1 that / one / than / is / This / expensive / cap / more / slightly

_____

2 will / than / much / a / taxi / longer / take / The bus

_____

3 do / far / than / My / scarier / I / finds / brother / spiders

_____

4 lot / cycling / energetic / Walking / is / than / less / a

_____

5 little / planned / Her / than / a / she'd / shopping / took / longer

_____

6 today / even / be / tomorrow / hotter / Apparently / will / than / !

_____

7 news / you / surprised / I / the / less / than / was / no / at

_____

4 Choose the correct answers (a–c) to complete the sentences.

1 A quarter is ___ much as 25%.
 a nowhere near as b almost as c just as

2 A second is ___ long as a minute.
 a not quite as b nothing like as c nearly as

3 Eleven forty-five p.m. is ___ late as midnight.
 a nearly as b nowhere near as c just as

4 Ninety-eight cents is ___ much as a euro.
 a just as b not quite as c nothing like as

5 Spain is ___ cold as Iceland.
 a nearly as b almost as c nowhere near as

6 The UK is ___ big as Russia.
 a almost as b nothing like as c not quite as

5 Complete the second sentence so that it means the same as the first.

1 That was the worst holiday I'd ever had!
 I'd never had a holiday as _____ one!

2 If we walk fast, we'll get there quicker.
 The _____ we'll get there.

3 Fast food used to be less healthy.
 Fast food is _____ used to be.

4 My jacket is nothing like as comfortable as yours.
 Your jacket is far _____ mine.

5 Your brother is the same age as me.
 Your brother is just _____ I am.

6 Indian food is far spicier than English food.
 English food is nothing _____ Indian food.

6 Complete the text with the words below.

as far fewer like more nowhere than the

Thanks to some films and TV shows, and certain types of music, many people still regard big cities in the USA as violent and crime-filled. However, recent reports show that they're [1]_____ near as dangerous as some people believe. Statistics for violent crime are nothing [2]_____ as bad as they were in the 1990s; the chance of being robbed or murdered is much lower [3]_____ in the 1990s when those crimes were far [4]_____ common than they are today. There are also slightly [5]_____ property crimes than forty years ago, with a drop of 2.8% being reported by some sources. Many inner-city areas once considered 'no-go' zones are [6]_____ more pleasant than they used to be, and cities generally are just as safe [7]_____ anywhere else in the world. The problem, of course, is that the more the media focuses on the few serious crimes, [8]_____ more afraid people become.

Keep calm!

I can understand emphasis.

1 🎧 **1.07** **Listen to sentences 1–5 and underline the emphasised word(s).**

1 Do you want tea or coffee?

2 'Is your number 07765?' 'No, it's 07756.'

3 That one's my jacket. The leather one.

4 'Is your name Mike?' 'No, it's Mark.'

5 Is that yours or mine?

> **Listening Strategy**
>
> When you listen, pay attention to the words that the speaker emphasises. Usually, a speaker uses emphasis:
>
> **a** to highlight new or important information, for example: I've lost my bag. It's a <u>cotton</u> bag, with <u>stripes</u>.
>
> **b** to put contrast two alternatives, for example: Was it <u>black</u> or <u>brown</u>?
>
> **c** to contradict what someone else has said, for example: Well, that's not <u>my</u> bag.

2 🎧 **1.08** **Read the Listening Strategy. Listen to six dialogues. Underline which words are emphasised in each one. Match each one with a reason from the Strategy (a, b or c).**

1 ___

A Which are your shoes?

B The ones with the laces.

2 ___

A I think I need a new phone.

B What? You've got a new phone?

A No, I said I need a new phone!

3 ___

A Can you give me a description of the thief, please?

B Yes, he was tall and he had blonde hair.

4 ___

A Shall we go shopping tomorrow or on Wednesday?

B Let's go tomorrow.

5 ___

A Don't forget your keys.

B But they're not my keys. They must be Edward's.

6 ___

A I'll get your suitcase. Is it the black one or the brown one?

B The brown one.

3 **Look at the lines of dialogue. Underline where the emphasis should go and say which reason from the Listening Strategy it matches with.**

1 Do you want a sandwich or a burger?

_____

2 A Is your locker number 14?

B No, number 40.

_____

3 Is this your drink or mine?

_____

4 Have you seen my scarf? It's green. Light green.

_____

5 A Are you going to the leisure centre this afternoon?

B No, this morning.

_____

6 My house has a red door and it's number 5.

_____

4 🎧 **1.09** **Listen and check your answers to exercise 3.**

5 🎧 **1.10** **Listen to the dialogue between two friends, Josh and Max. Choose the correct answers (a–d).**

1 At the beginning of the conversation, Josh

a ignores Max.

b feels ill.

c pretends that everything is OK.

d wants to go to chemistry class.

2 Josh tells Max

a that he's sorting out a problem.

b that he's made some new friends.

c that he's done something he regrets.

d not to tell his father.

3 Max's view is that

a Josh's dad will be angry with him.

b Josh's new friends are cool.

c Josh should confess to his father.

d Josh should challenge the boys.

4 Josh feels

a his father doesn't like Max.

b grateful for Max's support.

c he can't do anything about the situation.

d Max's advice isn't helpful.

2D Grammar

Infinitives and -ing forms

I can use infinitives and -ing forms.

1 Complete the sentences with the correct form of the verbs in brackets.

1 I don't remember _____ (meet) him before, although he looks familiar.

2 It's very rude when people stop _____ (talk) to you and answer their phone.

3 They meant _____ (get) off the bus at the last stop, but they missed it.

4 Do you regret not _____ (have) a party for your birthday?

5 My brother graduated from university and went on _____ (become) a vet.

6 If you stopped _____ (think) for a moment, I'm sure you'd find a solution.

7 He tried not _____ (make) too much noise when he got home.

2 Complete the sentences with the -ing form of the words below.

drive   finish   go   keep   live   lose   make

1 Sam discovered that _____ in a city was more expensive than in a village.

2 _____ to the gym twice a week will make a real difference to your fitness.

3 _____ the match was disappointing after the team had tried so hard.

4 My mother taught me that _____ fun of other people isn't nice.

5 _____ has become quite expensive as the cost of fuel continues to rise.

6 Don't worry about _____ the cleaning now – we can do it later.

7 _____ cool in the summer can be a real problem in some countries.

3 Match the sentence halves. Then complete the sentences with the -ing form or the infinitive of the verbs in brackets.

1 If you heard someone ☐

2 We have to get out – can't you hear ☐

3 It was a really strong earthquake; we felt ☐

4 We stood and watched the parade ☐

5 Did you see him ☐

6 I was horrified to feel ☐

a the ground _____ (shake) for several minutes.

b _____ (score) that last goal? It was amazing!

c something _____ (crawl) slowly up my leg as I was lying in bed.

d _____ (shut) the door then he must have already gone out.

e the fire alarm _____ (ring)?

f _____ (come) down the street while everyone cheered.

4 Choose the correct words to complete the text.

Many people would rather ¹**say / not say** anything when they experience bad service. For example, in a restaurant, they would sooner ²**pretend / not pretend** that their meal was fine, even if they didn't really enjoy it. But why ³**wait / not wait** until afterwards, then tell your friends about it? Surely you'd sooner ⁴**let / not let** those responsible know that there's a problem? For some reason, many of us think we'd better ⁵**cause / not cause** a fuss, but would you really rather ⁶**leave / not leave** a shop or restaurant feeling that you've been cheated? Why ⁷**be / not be** more assertive next time you have a genuine complaint?

5 Choose the correct answers (a–d) to complete the sentences.

1 If it's still snowing, why ___ a cab home?
   a not getting   b get   c not get   d getting

2 I'm sure my parents would rather ___ to the theatre than a night club!
   a going   b not going   c not go   d go

3 ___ in the corridor isn't allowed.
   a Running   b Not run   c Run   d Not running

4 She didn't mean ___ so much salt in the curry.
   a to put   b putting   c not to put   d not putting

5 Did you see anyone ___ suspiciously last night?
   a not behaving   b to behave   c behaving   d not behave

6 Would you sooner ___ at home this evening or go into town?
   a staying   b stay   c to stay   d not stay

6 Rewrite the sentences so that they have a similar meaning. Use the word in brackets.

1 If you don't understand, you should ask the teacher. (why)
   _____

2 Would you prefer chips or potatoes? (rather)
   _____

3 It wasn't her intention to upset anyone. (mean)
   _____

4 She forgot to post the parcel yesterday. (remember)
   _____

5 Don't spend ages on the computer before bed. (better)
   _____

6 Alex won't talk to him since they fell out. (stopped)
   _____

Preposition and noun phrases
I can use preposition + noun phrases.

1 Choose the correct answers (a–c) to complete the sentences.

1 It looks as though that shop has closed ___ – it's been empty for weeks now.
   a for now   b for one thing   c for good

2 The instructions should be clear, but if you're ___ , just ask someone.
   a in doubt   b in vain   c in effect

3 It was a horrible journey, but we got there ___ .
   a in all   b in the end   c in that case

4 If the staff here think you're ___ , they'll ask to see some identification.
   a under arrest   b under the impression   c under age

5 There's too much ___ to risk failing this exam.
   a at stake   b at fault   c at the moment

6 Do you have more ___ with your father or your mother?
   a in any case   b in common   c in that case

2 Write the words in brackets in the correct order to complete the sentences.

1 We were (the / impression / party / the / under / that) had been cancelled.

_____

2 Dan and Mia (a / have / for / been / while / dating).

_____

3 I'm afraid (a / moment / I'm / busy / the / bit / at). Can I call you back?

_____

4 I was going to buy the brown boots, (on / decided / second / but / thoughts / I) to get the black ones.

_____

5 'What do you like about living in Barcelona?' 'Well, (one / a / got / for / thing / it's) great nightlife.'

_____

6 I'll lend you this book (give / on / you / that / it / condition) back next week.

_____

3 Complete the sentences with the correct prepositions.

1 The ticket office sold me a return rather than a single _____ mistake.

2 Do you think Petra didn't invite us to her party _____ purpose?

3 I heard Finn got _____ trouble for not doing his homework.

4 Tina's not very keen on rock music – _____ fact, she can't stand it!

5 I'd like to see you later, but _____ course, if you're busy, that's fine.

6 No one was really _____ fault. It was just an accident.

4 Correct the mistakes in the phrases in bold. Tick the correct sentences.

1 It was a long day and **at the time** I got home I was exhausted. _____ ☐

2 The show doesn't start until eight, so we should still get there **in time**. _____ ☐

3 Joe and Lisa were always arguing and **at the end** they split up. _____ ☐

4 It's only **by the end** of the book that you learn the killer's identity. _____ ☐

5 I didn't realise it **by the time**, but the girl we met last night was Terry's sister. _____ ☐

6 We should have moved house **by the end** of the month. _____ ☐

5 Choose the correct words to complete the text.

How do you stop being friends with someone you no longer feel close to? If you've been friends for ¹**a while / one thing**, you may simply not have anything in ²**effect / common** any more. It doesn't mean anyone's at ³**fault / last**. If you've tried in ⁴**vain / control** to make things work, maybe it's best to end the friendship. Naturally, you don't want to hurt the other person, and if you're in any ⁵**time / doubt**, don't say or do anything you might regret. Perhaps your friend doesn't realise how you feel – they may be under ⁶**control / the impression** that everything's fine. You could talk to them and suggest not seeing each other for a few weeks, and in ⁷**time / fact** you'll know whether you want your friendship to continue or not.

VOCAB BOOST!

When you come across a new preposition + noun phrase, record it in your notebook under the preposition.

by: chance, mistake   *with*: (any) luck   *for*: a while

Then write an example sentence for each preposition + noun phrase to help you remember it:

With any luck, my parents will let me stay over at my friend's house tonight.

6 Read the *Vocab boost!* box. Complete the sentences with an appropriate noun and your own ideas.

1 Although I haven't done it for a _____ , I used to like _____ .

2 At the _____ , my favourite song is _____ .

3 The last time I was late for something was _____ . I couldn't get there on _____ because _____ .

4 In the future, I'd love to _____ . With any _____ , I'll be able to.

5 There are several reasons why I like my best friend. For one _____ , he/she _____ .

Solving crime

I can understand a text about different solutions to crime.

Revision: Student's Book page 26

1 Complete the newspaper article with the words below.

combat commit cut petty
prevention rate violent wave

Statistics show that the local police force has [1]_____ crime by 15%. However, this fall has only affected [2]_____ crimes such as murder. The crime [3]_____ for [4]_____ crimes such as shoplifting has gone up. This crime [5]_____ is affecting small shops and businesses. The police are working with shop owners to help them [6]_____ crime. They want them to install security cameras and participate in other crime [7]_____ efforts. Shopkeepers, however, are asking for more severe punishment for people who [8]_____ crimes and break the law.

2 Read the article. What problem could the technology mentioned in the article cause?

> **Reading Strategy**
>
> When matching questions with texts, remember that the key words from these questions may not appear in the text. The same information may be expressed in different words.

3 Read the Reading Strategy. Match paragraphs A–C with questions 1–6 below. Each paragraph may be matched with more than one question.

Which paragraph mentions ...

1 the disadvantages of a new technology? ☐
2 successful results from new technology? ☐
3 stopping criminals from getting away? ☐
4 a reduction in UK crime? ☐
5 police ignoring crime in some cases? ☐
6 a possible increase in crime rates? ☐

Robo-Cops

Police forces have always used technology to help them combat crime, but as collecting data and storing it becomes much easier, more and more police forces are using it to improve crime prevention and therefore to predict crime before it happens.

A Crime prevention software called PredPol helps the police predict where crimes are likely to occur. The software analyses years of data on the location, time and nature of crimes committed and predicts where and when crime is most likely to occur in the future. Police officers receive this information on the computers in their cars and they then spend more time in these areas. As a result, the increased police presence in these neighbourhoods has cut crime significantly. Crime figures for one area of Los Angeles, USA, were reduced by 12% in 2011 when police officers used crime prediction software. In the same year, burglaries were cut by 26% in Manchester, UK, using the same methods.

B As well as software that predicts crime, companies are also developing technology that will help police patrols catch criminals before they can leave town. By combining information such as the places where crimes frequently take place with the routes that allow the fastest escape, computers will direct patrols to where they can arrest criminals.

C However, although the makers of this technology claim it will help reduce crime rates, some people are not so sure. Not all crime is reported and if the police just focus on the neighbourhoods where most crime occurs, they will neglect others. Some experts claim that if police officers just pay attention to the information that has been stored in their devices, crime rates could actually rise in some areas.

Role-play

I can use diplomatic language in a discussion.

1 Match the sentence halves to make phrases for being diplomatic.

1	Can I have a word	a	feel that ...
2	Well, it's	b	it up, but ...
3	What did you have	c	something earlier.
4	I thought	d	we resolve this?
5	You must	e	with you about ... ?
6	So, how can	f	perhaps we could ...
7	I didn't want to bring	g	just that ...
8	You should have said	h	in mind?
9	And could we possibly	i	agree on ... ?

2 🎧 1.11 Listen to a student doing the task below. Tick the phrases in exercise 1 that you hear.

You are going on holiday with a friend for the first time. You are having problems with your friend. You feel you are taking all the responsibility. Talk with your friend about preparing for the trip and agree on a fair division of the tasks.

3 Put the following topics in the order they were discussed. What other topic was discussed?

a ☐ arranging insurance
b ☐ changing money and traveller's cheques
c ☐ organising transport to the airport
d ☐ booking and paying for the holiday

4 🎧 1.11 Read the Speaking Strategy. Listen again. Note examples of the strategies you hear.

Speaking Strategy

In a guided conversation, listen carefully to what the other person is saying and show interest.

Use structures like *Oh, dear ... Oh, I'm sorry ... I didn't realise ...* to empathise with the other person.

Use question tags, e.g. *... don't you? ... isn't it?... are you?* to gain agreement from the other person.

5 Match the question tags with the statements.

1 You've got the money, ___ ?
2 I paid for the ticket, ___ ?
3 Holidays aren't easy to organise, ___ ?
4 We hadn't booked the tickets, ___ ?
5 She can't be telling the truth, ___ ?

a had we?
b didn't I?
c can she?
d haven't you?
e are they?

6 Complete the second sentence so that it has a similar meaning to the first. Use *supposed to*.

1 It's important that we keep our travel documents safe at all times.

_____

2 It's expected that we leave a tip after the meal.

_____

3 We need to pay for the holiday by the 25th.

_____

7 Read the task below. Prepare your points about the issues below. Think of diplomatic phrases to use.

You are on holiday with a friend and are having problems with him/her. You feel you are taking all the responsibility for organising sightseeing trips, looking after the money and the luggage, and keeping the hotel room tidy. Talk with your friend about agree on how you can share these tasks.

1 organising sightseeing trips

_____

2 looking after the money and luggage

_____

3 keeping the hotel room tidy

_____

8 Think of one more topic to add and prepare a diplomatic phrase to use.

_____

9 Now do the task using your notes from exercises 7 and 8.

Essay: for and against
I can discuss both sides of a topic.

Preparation

> **Writing Strategy**
> When you write an essay, you need to ensure that it has a clear structure.
> **Paragraph 1:** introduction (stating the issue)
> **Paragraph 2:** arguments for the statement
> **Paragraph 3:** arguments against the statement
> **Paragraph 4:** summary, your own opinion

1 Read the Writing Strategy and the task below. What ideas do you expect to see in the essay?

'A problem shared is a problem halved.' Write an essay in which you offer arguments for and against discussing your personal problems with a friend.

2 Look at the phrases below. Find six more phrases for introducing arguments in the essay.

Introducing one side of the argument

1 _____ ...

It can be argued that ...

2 _____ ...

On the one hand, ...

3 _____ , ...

Furthermore, / Moreover, ...

Introducing the other side of the argument

However, ...

On the other hand, ...

4 _____

Having said that, ... / That said, ...

And yet, ...

5 _____

6 _____

3 Write the second sentence so that it has the same meaning as the first. Use the words in brackets.

1 I'll do the dishes if you clean the kitchen. (provided that)

_____

2 Despite the fact that he seems nice, I still don't trust him. (even though)

_____

3 Always try everything, despite the possibility it might not work out. (even if)

_____

4 He'll fix your bike if you lend it to him on Saturday. (on condition that)

_____

5 If I study all week, I'll pass the exam. (provided that)

_____

When people say that 'a problem shared is a problem halved,' they mean that it is good to talk about your issues with someone else. While this may be true, there can also be disadvantages to looking for help in this way.

The first advantage of talking to a friend about a personal problem is that you will gain sympathy and support from someone who cares about you. No one can deny that it is very helpful to have someone who listens to you and shows concern. Even if your friend can't offer practical advice, it will still make you feel better. It is also true that talking through a problem can help you come to a solution yourself.

So are there any disadvantages in confiding in friends in this way? Although it is true that it is helpful to share your problems with a friend, we should also remember that it is not a good idea to talk about your personal problems to everybody, or it can easily become gossip. It is important to pick one good friend that you can trust to keep your problem to themselves. Moreover, not everybody is kind, so you can end up feeling worse, unless you choose your friend wisely.

To sum up, talking about your problems to a friend is a very beneficial thing to do, provided that you pick the right person. A good friend is one you can trust.

Writing Guide

'You should always paddle your own canoe.' Write an essay in which you offer arguments for and against being totally independent, not asking for help and only relying on yourself.

4 Read the task and make notes.

Advantages _____

_____

Disadvantages _____

_____

5 Write your essay.

> **CHECK YOUR WORK**
> ◉ **Have you ...**
> ☐ followed the structure in the Writing Strategy?
> ☐ included key phrases for presenting your ideas?
> ☐ used a linker where possible?

Review Unit 2

Vocabulary

1 Complete the sentences with the words below.

alarmed bitter content disillusioned envious
humiliated stressed stunned

1 Beth is completely _____ with the course she's doing. It's nothing like she expected it to be.
2 My sister's a bit _____ about her wedding at the moment. She can't sleep at night.
3 I felt utterly _____ when I fell down the stairs. The whole class saw me and laughed!
4 I'm rather _____ of your new smartphone. I'd love to have one like that!
5 We were very _____ when my little brother disappeared. He was missing for over an hour.
6 My dad feels very _____ about losing his job. He thinks it was really unfair.
7 We were quite _____ to sit and wait. We weren't in any hurry.
8 Everybody was _____ by the tragic news.

Mark: ___ / 8

2 Complete the second sentence with an idiom containing the word in brackets.

1 I'm thrilled about winning the race. (moon)
   I'm _____ _____ _____ .
2 My mum is exasperated with my older brother. (hair)
   She's _____ _____ _____
   _____ .
3 Tom isn't sure if he should go to university. (minds)
   He's _____ _____ _____ about it.
4 Our first exam is today, so we're a bit anxious. (edge)
   We're all _____ _____ .
5 Waiting in queues makes me feel irritated. (nerves)
   It _____ _____ _____
   _____ .
6 Mia didn't get the job, so she's miserable. (dumps)
   She's _____ _____ _____
   _____ .

Mark: ___ / 6

Word Skills

3 Complete the sentences with the correct prepositions.

1 You're here ____ last. I've been waiting for ages!
2 My cousin's staying with us ____ now, until he finds his own place.
3 The future of that company is ____ doubt because it's losing money.
4 Let's meet at 8.00. ____ second thoughts, we'd better make it 7.15 so that we have time to get the tickets.

5 I was ____ the impression that it was going to rain today.
6 Sorry I'm late. I got on the wrong bus ____ mistake.
7 ____ course she'll be upset if you don't go to her party. You're her best friend!

Mark: ___ / 7

4 Complete the text about crime. Write one word in each gap.

Despite the fact that gun possession is legal in Iceland, [1]v_____ crimes, like murder, are almost unheard of. Around a quarter of the country's population owns a gun, but these are hardly ever used to [2]c_____ crimes. Pickpocketing and other [3]p_____ crimes are also rare. According to experts, the country has a tradition of crime [4]p_____ which stops any potential issues as soon as they are detected. In the 1970s, the government dealt with a minor crime [5]w_____ , involving drugs, by creating a separate drugs police force and drugs court. Today, there are relatively few hard drugs in Iceland compared to other countries. Politicians are currently attempting to [6]c_____ organised crime, which is on the increase, by passing new laws that will aid police in the fight.

Mark: ___ / 6

5 Complete the dialogue with diplomatic phrases.

A Rose, can I have a [1]_____ with you?
B Sure. What's up?
A I didn't want to [2]_____ it up, but you still owe me some money.
B Yes, I know. I'm really sorry about that.
A I thought [3]_____ we could talk about when you were planning on paying me back.
B I'm afraid I can't give it to you right now, Lily.
A Why's that?
B It's [4]_____ that my mum lost her job last month, so she's stopped giving me pocket money.
A Oh, no! You should have [5]_____ something earlier.
B You [6]_____ feel that you can't trust me any more!
A No, it's not that. I just couldn't understand why you hadn't paid me back. Now I know!

Mark: ___ / 6

Grammar

6 Complete the second sentence with a comparative or superlative so that it means the same as the first. Use the correct form of the adverb or adjecive from the first sentence.

1 You don't walk as fast as me.
   I walk _____ .
2 No one in my family sings as badly as my sister.
   My sister is _____ .
3 My best friend is more outgoing than me.
   I'm not _____ .

4 You'll be safe if you're cautious.
The more cautious you are, _____ .

5 My mum doesn't drive as carefully as my dad.
My dad drives _____ .

6 No one I know is more critical than my brother.
My brother is _____ .

Mark: ____ / 6

7 Look at the figures in the table. Then complete the sentences with the words below.

even   far   nearly   nothing   nowhere

The 100 most dangerous cities in the USA, 2015		
City	Population	Crime rate (per 1,000)
Camden, New Jersey	76,903	25.66
Chester, Pennsylvania	34,046	21.53
Detroit, Michigan	688,701	21.1
Philadelphia, Pennsylvania	1,553,165	11

1 The crime rate in Philadelphia is _____ near as high as it is in Camden.

2 Camden's population is _____ like as large as Philadelphia's.

3 Camden's population is quite small, but Chester's is _____ smaller.

4 Chester's population isn't _____ as big as Detroit's.

5 There are _____ more people living in Philadelphia than there are in Detroit.

Mark: ____ / 5

8 Complete the sentences with the infinitive, the infinitive without *to* or the *-ing* form of the verbs below.

argue   ask   get   pack   swim   waste

1 I've been meaning _____ about your job interview.

2 I think my brother has fallen out with his girlfriend. I heard them _____ last night.

3 _____ is not advisable when there is a storm warning.

4 I'd rather _____ a takeaway than cook dinner tonight.

5 Why _____ time in front of the TV when you could be outside in the sunshine?

6 I remembered _____ my tracksuit, but I didn't bring my trainers, so I can't go running.

Mark: ____ / 6

Use of English

9 Choose the correct answers (a–c) to complete the text.

Jet lag is a problem experienced after a long-haul flight. It occurs when people cross a number of time zones, disrupting their natural body clock [1]___ a while. One of [2]___ common symptoms is a disturbed sleep pattern, which means that they may want to sleep during the day [3]___ first. [4]___ confused and disoriented is another symptom. It usually takes one or two days to get the body clock [5]___ control again, although some people adjust to jet lag more [6]___ than others. The symptoms are usually [7]___ worse when going from west to east, because some time is lost during the journey, making the day of arrival [8]___ . This causes problems for travellers, who would sooner [9]___ sleep than try to force it. In general, the more time zones that are crossed, [10]___ severe the jet lag can become.

1 a during   b for   c in
2 a more   b most   c the most
3 a at   b by   c on
4 a Feel   b To feel   c Feeling
5 a over   b in   c under
6 a quick   b quicker   c quickly
7 a more   b much   c quite
8 a shortest   b shorter   c shortly
9 a delay   b to delay   c delaying
10 a more   b the more   c the most

Mark: ____ / 10

Total: ____ / 60

I can ...

Read the statements. Think about your progress and tick one of the boxes.

★ = I need more practice.   ★★★ = No problem!

★★ = I sometimes find this difficult.

	★	★★	★★★
I can describe feelings and emotions.			
I can make comparisons.			
I can understand emphasis.			
I can use infinitives and *-ing* forms.			
I can use preposition + noun phrases.			
I can understand a text about crime.			
I can use diplomatic language in a discussion.			
I can discuss both sides of a topic.			

Reading

1 Read the Strategy and look at the sentences in exercise 2. Find the words that indicate the focus of each sentence.

2 Read the text. Four sentences have been removed. Match missing sentences A–E with gaps 1–4. There is one extra sentence.

Dying for a selfie

Most of us have taken a selfie at one time or another, be it a photo of ourselves in a beautiful place, during a performance by our favourite band, or on a memorable night out with friends. Even monarchs, prime ministers and presidents have been seen in the news grinning inanely at the screen of a smartphone. ¹_____ In several cases, this action has had disastrous consequences.

Take, for example, the Spaniard who was killed by a bull while he was taking a selfie during the annual bull run in a village near his hometown. ²_____ Incidents such as these led to the death toll from selfie-related incidents reaching double figures for the first time in 2015, overtaking the number of victims of shark attacks. Most of the cases involve people taking selfies while posing with animals, or falling from high places.

Despite the risks, social media is full of pictures featuring near misses that could have been fatal under other circumstances. Under the caption 'Most dangerous selfie ever', a woman posing at a stadium can be seen narrowly avoiding being hit in the head by a baseball approaching her. ³_____ What is even more worrying, however, is that the woman herself dares others to better the shot, seemingly overlooking the fact that by doing so, she is endangering the lives of her 'friends' as well.

In response to the increasing threat posed by the selfie, the authorities have started to take action. National parks, such as the Waterton Canyon in Denver, Colorado, have closed their gates to visitors who have been getting too close to the bears to get them in the photo. ⁴_____ But if instructions like these are really necessary, then perhaps it is about time we asked ourselves which is more important, a 'like' or a life?

A Or the Singaporean tourist who died when he fell from cliffs on the coast of Bali.

B The alternative to taking unnecessary risks is to use Photoshop to create outrageous pictures.

C The Russian Interior Ministry has launched a public education campaign advising selfie-takers against balancing on dangerous surfaces or posing with their pets, among other things.

D But today, more and more people are putting their lives at risk in an attempt to get the most shocking picture to share on social media.

E Yet the photo has received thousands of 'likes', and the comments below it suggest that this behaviour is something to be admired.

Listening

3 Read the Strategy and look at exercise 4. What are the questions asking you to do: define the gist, identify intention, determine context, or distinguish fact from opinion?

4 🎧 1.12 You will hear three texts twice. Choose the correct option, A, B, or C.

Text 1

1 Which of the following is stated in the talk as a fact and not an opinion?

  A The police will only pay a visit if more than one complaint has been made.

  B People should be quiet for eight hours every night.

  C Neighbours must be warned about noisy birthday parties in advance.

Text 2

2 Where does the conversation take place?

  A Outside a block of flats.

  B In somebody's living room.

  C Inside a lift.

Text 3

3 Why have the woman's neighbours complained about her hedge?

  A It makes their houses extremely dark.

  B It is two or three metres higher than it should be.

  C It blocks the view from their windows.

Use of English

5 Read the Strategy and look at the sentence below. Which is the correct option? Why are the other options wrong?

It's far more difficult to find a job now than it ___ to be.

  a have   b used   c wants   d was

Exam Skills Trainer

6 Read the text and complete the gaps. Choose the correct answer, A, B, C, or D.

Keeping a country clean

One problem that all the countries in the world have ¹___ common is litter. In ²___ to get the situation under control in the UK, the government ³___ a national spring cleaning day, which takes place every year on the first day of spring. The aim is to convey the message that local areas will be ⁴___ places to work and live if people look after them. Ministers believe that chewing gum companies and fast food outlets are partly responsible for the problem and so they are hoping to persuade them ⁵___ on the day. Studies carried out by the organisation Keep Britain Tidy have shown that more than half the population is guilty of ⁶___ litter, leaving it to city councils to clean up the mess. This means ⁷___ cash from fundamental areas, such as care of the elderly, to foot the bill. It has been calculated that more than £800 million every year is spent on cleaning city streets. The government hopes to change people's behaviour by making dropping litter ⁸___ as unacceptable as illegal parking.

1	**A** at	**B** for	**C** in	**D** on
2	**A** a case	**B** an intention	**C** a trial	**D** an effort
3	**A** had organised	**B** organised	**C** organises	**D** has organised
4	**A** better	**B** more	**C** best	**D** much
5	**A** helping	**B** to help	**C** help	**D** helped
6	**A** drop	**B** dropping	**C** dropped	**D** to drop
7	**A** diverting	**B** to divert	**C** divert	**D** diverted
8	**A** even	**B** far	**C** just	**D** much

Speaking

> ### Strategy
> To sound natural, use language which is typical for spoken interaction, e.g. phrasal verbs (*get on, turn up*), discourse markers (*you know, actually, as I was saying, what I mean is*), colloquial expressions (*in hot water, couch potato*), or hedging words (*may, might, could, quite, a bit, sort of, I guess*).

7 Read the Strategy and look at sentences 1–6. Replace the underlined words with the more colloquial alternatives below.

a drag   but   get in touch with   kind of busy
loads and loads of   put up with

1 Sorry, I'm <u>occupied</u> today. _____
2 How can you <u>tolerate</u> this mess? _____
3 I'll <u>contact</u> him tomorrow. _____
4 Good idea; <u>however,</u> I'm not around on Monday. _____
5 There are <u>many</u> exercises to do. _____
6 Studying grammar is <u>very boring</u>. _____

8 As part of a school exchange, a student from the UK is staying with you. You are having problems with the student and you need to establish some clear rules. Discuss the following points and come to an agreement on each one.

- leaving the lights on
- clearing up after meals
- talking on the phone late at night
- using your laptop

9 Summarise what you have agreed for each point in exercise 8.

Writing

> ### Strategy
> Always start by planning your arguments. Write down three or four ideas for and three or four against the topic. Choose the best two arguments for each side of the issue, and develop them by adding a comment or providing an example.

10 Read the Strategy and look at the arguments below against sharing a flat with a sibling. Develop the arguments. Use the questions to help you.

1 It may mean no privacy for both of you.
Will you be able to keep your 'private life' away from your sibling? What might they report back to your parents?

2 It will lead to arguments over household chores.
Why will it be difficult to share out the chores? How might this affect your relationship?

3 There may be pressure to hang out constantly.
Why will it be difficult to have space for yourself? What might your sibling think if you refuse to go out with him/her one evening?

11 Read the task below and write your essay.

Some parents have access to their teenage children's social media accounts and control their online activities. Write an essay in which you discuss arguments for and against the attitude of these parents.

3 Customs and culture

Vocabulary

A Express yourself
I can describe body language, gestures and movement.

1 Match the gestures below with the pictures (1–6).

cover your mouth   cross your legs   give a thumbs up
point   scratch your head   shrug your shoulders

1 _____   2 _____

3 _____   4 _____

5 _____   6 _____

2 Which parts of the body do you use to make the following gestures and expressions? Put the words below in the correct column.

nod   point   pout   scowl   shake   wave   wink

head	face	hand

3 Complete the text with the correct form of the words below.

bite   frown   grin   nod   shake   yawn

Mark was really nervous before the Spanish speaking exam! He either fidgeted and played with a pen or he ¹_____ his fingernails. He also started ²_____ , even though he wasn't sleepy! When he looked at me, he ³_____ nervously, but there was nothing funny about the situation. Then, in the exam, instead of answering the examiner's questions with a 'yes' or 'no' and an explanation, he just ⁴_____ or ⁵_____ his head! Luckily, the examiner ⁶_____ at these answers, so Mark got the message and started speaking in Spanish.

4 Complete the sentences with the words below.

annoyance   anxiety   boredom   disgust   friendliness
surprise

1 People will see it as a sign of _____ if you are yawning all the time.
2 If you bite your nails, people will think it's a sign of _____ .
3 People will say you're showing _____ if you purse your lips.
4 People will see it as a sign of _____ if you wave.
5 If you grimace, people will say you're showing _____ .
6 If you raise your eyebrows, people will think it's a sign of _____ .

5 🎧 1.13 Listen to four speakers. Match sentences A–E with speakers 1–4. There is one extra sentence.

This speaker:

A gets a shock when she hears some news. ☐
B thinks some instructions cause confusion. ☐
C is disappointed with someone's performance. ☐
D is indifferent to an activity. ☐
E feels shame for what has happened. ☐

6 🎧 1.13 Listen again and complete the sentences with the emotions below. There are two extra emotions.

fear   ignorance   indifference   interest   shock   surprise

1 Speaker 1 feels _____ at their friend's wish to go and see a musical.
2 Speaker 2 expresses his _____ about how he should use electrical devices.
3 Speaker 3 talks about someone who uses _____ to try and obtain things.
4 Speaker 4 says someone has to show more _____ in their work.

7 Match the words below with the descriptions. There are two extra words.

clear your throat   cough   gasp   hiccup   sigh   slurp
sneeze   sniff   snore   tut

1 Some people do this in their sleep. _____
2 We often do these three things when we have a cold.
_____ , _____ , _____
3 People sometimes do this before they speak. _____
4 It is considered rude to do this in some cultures when you eat dishes such as soup. _____
5 We make this sound when we want to show disapproval of something. _____
6 We make this sound to express both sadness and pleasure. _____

Grammar
Modals: present and future
I can use modals to talk about the present, and future possibility

1 Write the words in the correct order to make sentences.

1 a / you / guidebook / buy / needn't

_____

2 book / table / need / don't / we / to / a

_____

3 apologise / her / ought / she / to / behaviour / for

_____

4 we / take / are / to / a / supposed / gift / ?

_____

5 a / don't / to / tip / you / have / leave

_____

6 eat / your / hand / have / you / to / with / right

_____

2 Match the sentence halves.

1 This is supposed ☐   4 He needn't ☐
2 It can ☐   5 It can't ☐
3 You'll be able to ☐   6 Everyone ought ☐

a take a boat trip tomorrow if the weather improves.
b be easy travelling on your own as you may get lonely.
c to be the most beautiful city in the world.
d to keep an open mind about other cultures.
e be extremely hot in Australia at Christmas.
f check out of the hotel yet.

3 Choose the correct verbs (a–d) to complete the text.

Customs in different countries ¹___ vary widely and it's
sometimes difficult to know how to behave. If you're
visiting Turkey, for example, and you're asked to
dinner at someone's house, you ²___ take a gift. It ³___
be anything expensive – flowers or pastries are a good
idea. Try to eat everything on your plate or you ⁴___
upset your host! Remember that you ⁵___ point at people
with your finger – it's considered very rude. And you
⁶___ show the bottoms of your feet for the same reason.
Watch what other people do and follow their example
and you ⁷___ be fine!

1	a ought to	b can	c must	d should
2	a need	b might not	c mustn't	d ought to
3	a must	b needn't	c has to	d may
4	a could	b can	c should	d are able to
5	a should	b mustn't	c don't need to	d have to
6	a may	b are supposed to	c shouldn't	d must
7	a can	b have to	c should	d might

4 Correct the mistakes in the sentences. Tick the correct sentences.

1 The winters are able to be very cold in Austria.
_____ ☐

2 When we visit Norway next month, we should see the Northern Lights. _____ ☐

3 This needs be the right house – it's got a green door and blue curtains, just as Lara described. _____ ☐

4 That man mustn't be Ella's dad – he looks too old.
_____ ☐

5 This can be the last time I see you! I have to see you again!
_____ ☐

6 You have to wait for me if you're in a hurry – I'll see you there!
_____ ☐

7 In a year's time, I'll be able to drive. _____ ☐

5 Complete the second sentence so that it means the same as the first. Use modal verbs.

1 Sometimes our neighbours are very noisy.
Our neighbours _____ very noisy.

2 You may not have another opportunity to see this film.
This _____ last opportunity to see this film.

3 I'm sure we're not late because we left on time.
We left on time so _____ late.

4 Surely you recognise that woman from TV?
_____ that woman from TV!

5 I hope it'll be possible to go skiing in the winter.
I hope I _____ go skiing in the winter.

6 It's possible that tomorrow's match will be cancelled.
Tomorrow's match _____ cancelled.

6 Complete the text with the words below.

able   might   mustn't   needn't   should (x2)   supposed

Every country around the world has its own customs
and traditions, usually connected with bringing good
luck or trying to avoid bad luck. For example, in
Japan, if a beggar comes to your house, you are
¹_____ to throw salt where they've been,
otherwise you ²_____ have bad luck. In Brazil,
you ³_____ place a small container of salt in
the corner of the house and this ⁴_____ bring
you good luck. In India, if there is a birth or death,
the family members ⁵_____ go to a temple or
light a lamp in the house for fifteen days. Unmarried
people in Russia should avoid sitting at the corner
of the table or they won't be ⁶_____ to find
a life partner. And in Vietnam, you ⁷_____
take an expensive gift to a wedding; in fact, two less
expensive ones are better!

When in Rome ...
I can identify different types of listening text.

Listening Strategy
As you listen, focus on features that tell you what type of text you are hearing (e.g. news, interview, advertisement, notice, story, review, joke, etc.) and what the topic is. Such clues include register (formal or informal), subject vocabulary or the speaker's tone of voice.

1 Write informal sentences with the same meaning. Use the words in brackets.

1 Good morning. (there)

_____

2 It's a pleasure to meet you. (good)

_____

3 Allow me to introduce you to some of my colleagues. (meet)

_____

4 Could I fetch you a coffee at all? (fancy)

_____

5 It's very kind of you to offer. (why)

_____

6 It was a pleasure to meet you. (great)

_____

2 🎧 **1.14** Listen to extracts from conversations. For each one, decide if it is formal (F) or informal (I). Then write the words or phrases that helped you decide.

1 ___ _____

2 ___ _____

3 ___ _____

4 ___ _____

5 ___ _____

6 ___ _____

7 ___ _____

8 ___ _____

9 ___ _____

10 ___ _____

3 🎧 **1.15** Read the Listening Strategy. Then listen to extracts 1–6 and match them with text types a–f.

a an interview ☐   **d** a joke ☐
b a story ☐   **e** a play ☐
c a chat between friends ☐   **f** a review ☐

4 🎧 **1.16** Listen to the beginnings of four texts. Who is speaking? Match text types 1–4 with people A–F. There are two extra people.

A entertainer ☐   **D** student and professor ☐
B media presenter ☐   **E** colleagues ☐
C friends ☐   **F** tourist guide and tourist ☐

5 🎧 **1.17** Listen to the four texts in full and choose the correct answers (a–c).

1 In text 1, what is the student particularly enthusiastic about?
  a The chance to study science using a foreign language.
  b The challenge of learning new vocabulary quickly.
  c Opportunities to improve her French outside of her lessons.

2 In text 2, what is Stella's main worry about her friends?
  a That they won't be able to find work in the USA.
  b That Joe won't understand Maria's problems.
  c That Maria will not be happy in the USA.

3 In text 3, why is the comedian planning to do shows abroad?
  a To help people abroad improve their English.
  b To show that London is home to the best comedians.
  c To show that English comedians can speak other languages too.

4 In text 4, what is the woman doing?
  a She's selling tickets for the London Eye.
  b She's giving advice on London attractions.
  c She's offering guided tours.

Past modals
I can use modal verbs to talk about past actions.

1 Choose the correct options (a–c) to complete the sentences.

1 I can't get this tablet to work; I ___ read the instructions properly.
  a oughtn't to have   b can't have   c shouldn't have

2 I ordered the DVD a week ago so it ___ arrived here by now.
  a should have   b could have   c may have

3 I can't find my phone anywhere. I ___ left it at school.
  a should have   b may have   c ought to have

4 Julie's not at home. She ___ decided to go out after all.
  a was supposed to have   b must have   c ought to have

5 You ___ promised to help Ed if you didn't have time.
  a mustn't have   b couldn't have   c shouldn't have

6 You ___ told me you'd eaten all the biscuits! I'd have got some more.
  a may have   b must have   c might have

2 Complete the sentences with up to five words, including the words in brackets.

1 Someone _____ (might / told / me) there was a hole in my jumper!

2 Sandra _____ (supposed / be / here) by now. I wonder where she is.

3 You _____ (ought / have / gone) swimming if you have a cold.

4 Wendy didn't look very happy when I saw her; she _____ (could / worried / about) going to the dentist.

5 The fridge is empty; Mum _____ (can't / been / the) shops yet.

6 Last night _____ (must / been / cold) – the lake's frozen.

3 Complete the email with the correct form of the verbs below.

can't   could (x2)   may   must   should

To: artur@email.com

Hi Artur

Well, we're still enjoying our trip to England. We're staying in a great city – but someone ¹_____ told us that there was going to be a festival here yesterday! Perhaps we ²_____ realised something was happening, because a lot of the hotels were full. The festival was great! According to the local paper, this ³_____ been the biggest crowd they'd ever had. The streets were packed. I reckon there ⁴_____ been about 30,000 people there. There was a fancy dress parade too; if we'd known, we ⁵_____ got dressed up. Mind you, some of the people ⁶_____ been very comfortable as some of the costumes looked really hot! I bought you a souvenir. I'll see you in a couple of weeks.

Lena

4 Complete the sentences with *needn't have* or *didn't need to* and the verb in brackets. In which sentences are both modals possible?

1 I managed to mend my sunglasses so luckily I _____ (get) a new pair.

2 It was sunny so we _____ (take) an umbrella.

3 We _____ (catch) a cab as my mum gave us a lift.

4 Alison _____ (buy) a ticket – I had a spare one.

5 I _____ (worry) about the test – when I saw the paper I realised I knew all the answers.

6 You _____ (walk) the dog; we walked it this morning.

5 Complete the sentences with the words in the box.

could   didn't need to   needn't   ought not to
was supposed to

1 You _____ have reminded me to do the homework – I did it last night.

2 Tanya _____ be here half an hour ago. Where is she?

3 We _____ have told Jenny about Luca's party. He didn't want her to know about it.

4 Someone _____ have warned me that the band's new album was so awful!

5 They knew the way so they _____ ask for directions.

6 Rewrite the sentences using the words in brackets.

1 Lunch was provided so it wasn't necessary for them to take sandwiches. (need)

_____

2 She studied hard so she probably passed the exam. (should)

_____

3 I think he's foreign so it's possible he didn't understand you. (might)

_____

4 John isn't in Rome – I saw him earlier. (can't)

_____

5 It would have been better if you'd listened to my advice. (ought)

_____

6 Why didn't you introduce me to your friends? (might)

_____

American English

I can recognise differences between American and British English.

1 Write the American English equivalents of the words in bold.

1 Why don't you borrow my **mobile** to call your mum?

_____

2 I'll have to buy a new pair of **trainers** soon; these are almost worn out. _____

3 Don't forget to take a **torch** when we go camping; it'll be dark at night. _____

4 Taking the **motorway** will make our journey quicker.

_____

5 Would you like a **biscuit** with your tea? _____

6 If everyone's finished, I'll ask the waiter for the **bill**.

_____

7 Her dog's very well trained and always walks on the **pavement**. _____

8 I'm too tired to walk up the stairs; let's take the **lift**.

_____

2 Complete the text with American English words. The first letters are given.

This year, my parents decided not to go away in the summer, but to wait until the ¹F_____ to go on ²v_____ for a few days. They'd always wanted to have a city break, so they looked online for somewhere to stay and found accommodation near the center of Manhattan. The ³a_____ they rented was quite small, but the bedrooms were big and there was plenty of space in the ⁴c_____ for their clothes. There was also a small ⁵y_____ where they could eat breakfast outside. Of course the ⁶t_____ in New York is great for getting around; they could walk to most of the sights or take the ⁷s_____ for longer journeys across town.

3 Circle the American English spellings.

1 In some US states, you only need to be fourteen to hold a driver's **licence / license**.

2 In the **neighbourhood / neighborhood** of Beverly Hills, many homes are worth over $10 million.

3 The world's first commercial flight took place in 1914; the **airplane / aeroplane** flew for 23 minutes.

4 New York's oldest **theater / theatre** is the Lyceum, which opened in 1903.

5 The **colors / colours** of the US flag are the same as Australia's and the UK's.

6 The international Erasmus **organization / organisation** has already helped over three million students study in different countries.

4 🎧 **1.18 Listen to the different words being pronounced. Write A (American) or B (British).**

1 advertisement ☐
2 brochure ☐
3 garage ☐
4 tomato ☐
5 vitamins ☐
6 yoghurt ☐
7 zebra ☐

VOCAB BOOST!

British English often keeps the spelling of words that have come from languages such as Latin, Greek, or French, while the American English equivalent often reflects how the words sound when spoken, e.g. *centre / center, dialogue / dialog*. Keep a note of equivalent spellings in a vocabulary notebook. You can practise any difference in pronunciation at the same time.

5 Read the *Vocab boost!* box. Label the columns *American* and *British*. Then complete the equivalent spellings. Add examples from exercise 3 and more of your own.

1 _____ English	2 _____ English
behaviour	3 _____
4 _____	cancelation
centimetre	5 _____
6 _____	liter
memorise	7 _____
8 _____	marvelous
9 _____	savory

6 Rewrite the American English sentences in British English using the correct vocabulary and spelling. Use a dictionary to help you.

1 It's an offense to smoke on the subway.

_____

2 I bought this awesome purse for my friend's birthday.

_____

3 It seems tonight's movie has been canceled.

_____

4 Can you get me a liter of water from the faucet, please?

_____

5 There's a strange odor from the car – I hope the gas isn't leaking.

_____

6 Sorry, I hadn't realized you were waiting in the line.

_____

Revision: Student's Book page 36

1 **Match 1–5 with a–e to make compound adjectives.**

1	home	a	set
2	long	b	throated
3	thin-	c	haired
4	deep-	d	boned
5	low-	e	made

2 **Read the review. Which three writing skills (a–e) does the reviewer say Hosseini has?**

a He writes good dialogues between the characters.

b He provides good descriptions.

c He uses a wide range of vocabulary.

d He is able to explain a difficult topic to readers.

e The story moves along at a good speed.

Reading Strategy

- When you do a gapped sentences task, first read the text quickly to find out what it is about.
- Then read the text more carefully and think about what information is missing in each gap.
- Look at the parts of the text before and after each gap to find words or information that link it to one of the missing sentences.
- Pay attention to vocabulary and grammar structures, which may also provide ideas.
- After you have matched a sentence to each gap, check that the remaining sentence doesn't match any of the gaps.

3 **Read the Reading Strategy. Then read the text again. Match sentences A–E with gaps 1–4. There is one extra sentence.**

A *The Kite Runner* then becomes a story of Amir's journey in search of a way to make up for what he did.

B The fighting seems to go on forever, but there is a feeling at the end that good will defeat evil eventually.

C We follow the development of the boys' close relationship, but it is shattered by completely different events.

D The story not only provides Western readers with an insight into a culture and a country, but it is also a lesson in how to write a bestseller.

E As well as portraying the close relationship between two boys, Amir and Hassan, it describes the last peaceful days of Afghanistan, before revolution and war would destroy the country.

▌▌ BOOK REVIEW

The Kite Runner by Khaled Hosseini

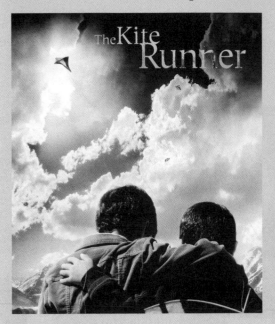

Khaled Hosseini's first novel, *The Kite Runner*, is a powerful story of friendship, betrayal and suffering. It is set in Kabul, the capital of Afghanistan, in the seventies, then a relatively liberal and open-minded city. ¹__

Although the novel describes dramatic political events, it is Amir's close friendship with Hassan, the son of his father's servant, which catches our attention. Hassan serves his friend breakfast every morning and then stays to clean the house while Amir is driven to school. Hassan does not resent his friend's much more comfortable life and he is a loyal companion. However, Amir betrays him, an act that will make Amir feel guilty even when he and his father have escaped to America and left Hassan and the war behind. ²__ It is a journey that takes him back to his home country and forces him to face the suffering that the people he left behind have to live with.

Hosseini describes Afghanistan in a way that brings the country to life, and his writing style is always clear and easy to follow. The story moves along at a fast pace and takes us on an incredibly exciting journey from the joy and happiness of the boys' youth to the anxiety and fear of the war. ³__ Hosseini has demonstrated great skill in managing to take such a complicated theme and produce a novel that readers all over the world find hard to put down.

The Kite Runner is a dramatic novel that is full of action and emotion and that, despite the war that erupts and destroys people's lives, offers hope. ⁴__ Much of the story is set in a country that has suffered greatly, but the ending suggests that there might be a better future both for the characters and for Afghanistan. One can only hope that this is the case.

★★★★★

Topic-based presentation

I can talk about a cultural event or festival.

1 🎧 **1.19** Listen to a student doing the task below. Which of the four prompts (A–D) does she not mention?

> Look at the pictures. Then talk for about one minute about how people in your country celebrate International Women's Day.
> **A** What is the history behind the celebration?
> **B** Do people usually give or receive gifts and/or cards?
> **C** Are there any other annual traditions?
> **D** Do you personally take part in any celebrations?

Speaking Strategy 1
Make sure that you mention all of the prompts in the task. Learn some useful phrases for changing the subject or moving on to the next point.

2 Read Speaking Strategy 1. Complete phrases 1–4 with the words below.

far   now   something   subject

1 As _____ as the history of the event is concerned, ...
2 Turning _____ to the topic of ...
3 That brings me to the _____ of ...
4 There's _____ else I'd like to talk about: ...

3 🎧 **1.19** Listen again. Match phrases 1–4 from exercise 2 with endings a–f below. There are two extra endings.

a ___ marches on International Women's Day.
b ___ home-made greetings cards.
c ___ national holidays.
d ___ gifts, the most common one is flowers.
e ___ I'm not really an expert.
f ___ celebrations at school.

Speaking Strategy 2
When you don't know or can't remember the words you need, use phrases for paraphrasing so that you can explain what you mean in other words.

4 Read Speaking Strategy 2. Match the sentence halves.

1 It would be called x   a you (wear / eat / drink, etc.).
2 It's like x,   b kind of ...
3 It's something   c in my language.
4 It's a   d but (bigger / smaller, etc.).

5 Choose two things you can see in the photos on this page. Describe them using phrases from exercise 4.

_____
_____
_____
_____

> Look at the pictures. Then talk for about one minute about how people in your country celebrate New Year.
> **A** Does food or drink play a part in the celebration?
> **B** Do people usually give or receive gifts and/or cards?
> **C** Are there any other traditions?
> **D** What do you personally usually do to celebrate?

6 Look at the task above. Make notes for each of the four prompts.

1 Does food or drink play a part in the celebration?
_____
2 Do people usually give or receive gifts and/or cards?
_____
3 Are there any other traditions?
_____
4 What do you personally usually do to celebrate?
_____

7 Now do the task, using your notes from exercise 6.

A blog post
I can write a blog post.

A newspaper has published an online article suggesting that the local bus service into town is no longer required. Write a blog post outlining the advantages of the bus service, giving an account of when you last used it.

Preparation

1 Read the task above and the article below.

In which paragraph does the writer ...
1 describe a personal experience? ___
2 list reasons to keep the bus service? ___
3 give a reason for writing the letter? ___
4 suggest that money isn't the only consideration? ___

 DON'T BAN THE BUSES!

A Without buses, local residents will be, quite simply, stranded. Your article suggested that the service into town costs the council too much money and is not used enough. As a young person who relies on the bus, I'd like to outline some arguments against this view.

B I strongly disagree with the suggestion that there is no value in continuing the bus service. Firstly, not everyone has a car, so won't a public service always be required? Secondly, the bus gives teenagers necessary independence and the ability to travel. Thirdly, the bus is much more environmentally friendly than cars. Therefore the cost must be weighed against the cost to the environment if there were no bus service.

C The last time I took the bus was last weekend. I always go by bus into the town centre with my friends on Saturdays. Travelling to town, I chatted to the other passengers. They were all in agreement that the service was still necessary and that they would have great difficulty in managing without it. In fact, the point was made that if there were *more* buses, the service would be used even more.

D In my view, rather than being unnecessary, the bus service is essential for those in the community without a car. They are also invaluable for bringing and keeping communities together. How can you put a price on that?

> **Writing Strategy**
> Make a plan for your blog post so you allow enough space to include every element from the task instructions. Remember to include a good introduction and a summary.

2 Read the Writing Strategy and find the two paragraphs in the blog post that cover the elements required in the task.

3 Complete the sentences with the correct form of the verbs in brackets.
1 Having _____ (run) to catch the bus, I got to the party in time.
2 _____ (travel) together on the train, we often chatted.
3 As the tourists _____ (arrive), the tourist office opened.
4 After _____ (finish) his coffee, he went to the cinema.
5 _____ (wait) for you, I read a book.
6 Having _____ (make) the cake, they began to eat it.
7 After _____ (swim) in the river, they sunbathed for an hour.

4 Find an example of one of the structures from exercise 3 in the blog post.

Writing Guide

A local newspaper published an online article suggesting that the tourist office in town is an unnecessary expense. Write a blog post outlining the advantages of the tourist office and giving an account of a time you used it with a foreign visitor.

5 Read the task above. Make some notes for a) the advantages of the tourist office and b) your account.

Advantages _____
_____
_____
Your account _____
_____
_____

6 Write your blog post. Follow the paragraph plan in exercise 1.

> **CHECK YOUR WORK**
> **Have you ...**
> ☐ structured your blog post in four paragraphs?
> ☐ written equally about both required elements?
> ☐ included a sequencing clause in your description?

3 Review Unit 3

Vocabulary

1 Complete the sentences with a verb from A and a body part from B.

A bowed covered crossed folded gave pursed raised shrugged

B arms eyebrows fingers head lips mouth shoulders thumbs

1 Mike's parents _____ him a _____ up to encourage him to do his best in the race.
2 My brother _____ his _____ across his chest defensively when my parents asked where he'd been.
3 The teacher _____ her _____ in disbelief at Aaron's excuse for not doing the homework.
4 On the day of her driving test, Olivia _____ her _____ for luck as she was getting into the car.
5 My grandmother _____ her _____ in disapproval when my brother showed her his new tattoo.
6 The boy _____ his _____ in shame when he was expelled from school.
7 The girl _____ her _____ as she yawned during the ceremony.
8 I didn't know the answer so I just _____ my _____ .

Mark: ___ / 8

2 Match 1–6 with a–f.

1 I can't sleep.
2 Eat your soup properly.
3 Blow your nose!
4 Ah, you don't approve.
5 Have a drink of water.
6 Are you allergic to that?

a You're sniffing.
b You're tutting.
c You're coughing.
d You're slurping.
e You're snoring.
f You're sneezing.

Mark: ___ / 6

Word Skills

3 Replaced the underlined American English words with British English words.

1 Could we have the <u>check</u>, please? _____
2 Oh no! I can't find my <u>cellphone</u>. _____
3 An apple is better for you than a bag of <u>chips</u>. _____
4 Would you like a <u>cookie</u>? _____
5 Shall we go by bus or take the <u>subway</u>? _____
6 Have you got a <u>flashlight</u>? There's no electricity. _____
7 There's been an accident on the <u>highway</u>. _____
8 Did you get any <u>gas</u> before we left? _____

Mark: ___ / 8

4 Complete the sentences with compound adjectives formed using the words in brackets.

1 I love listening to my uncle. He's got a very rich voice and a _____ laugh. (throat)
2 My neighbour's high forehead and _____ eyes mean he has a rather memorable face. (set)
3 Your grandmother is absolutely tiny! She must be very _____ . (bone)
4 There must be a rock concert tonight. There are hundreds of _____ men queuing outside the venue. (hair)

Mark: ___ / 4

5 Complete the dialogues with the phrases below.

In other words   It's a kind of
It's something you   what it's called

Dani We're having a birthday party for my little brother tomorrow.
John That's nice. Is he going to have a – oh – I don't know ¹_____ in English.
Dani Cake?
John No. ²_____ box with sweets in it.
Dani A present?
John No! ³_____ hang up high and the children hit it to get the sweets. ⁴_____ , when they break it, the sweets fall out.
Dani Oh, a piñata! Yes, there's going to be a piñata. It wouldn't be a party without one!

Mark: ___ / 4

Grammar

6 Complete the text with the words below.

you don't have   you must   you mustn't   you needn't
you're supposed   you should

> If you're planning on visiting Australia in the future, here are a few tips. ¹_____ have a visa to enter the country, unless you're an Australian or New Zealand citizen. ²_____ to register with the police while you're there, but ³_____ to leave before your visa expires. ⁴_____ take fresh or packaged food into the country, and plants and seeds are also banned. The greatest risk to personal safety comes from the sun, which, in Australia, is very strong. ⁵_____ spend all of your visit indoors, but ⁶_____ stay out of the sun in the middle of the day, when it's at its strongest.

Mark: ___ / 6

7 Choose the correct words to complete the dialogue.

A Spring at last! It ¹**can** / **may** / **must** be your birthday soon.

B It is – on 5 April. I'm having a barbecue that weekend.

A You ²**can't** / **may** / **should** be serious!

B Why? What's the problem?

A It ³**can't** / **might** / **must** rain!

B Do you think so?

A Yes. April ⁴**can** / **should** / **must** be very showery, you know.

B Perhaps. It ⁵**can't** / **must** / **should** be all right, though. It didn't rain last year.

A But you won't ⁶**be able to** / **can** / **could** eat in the garden if the weather's bad!

B No problem. We'll eat in the house instead!

Mark: ____ / 6

8 Complete the sentences with *must have*, *might* (*not*) *have*, *can't have*, *should have*, or *shouldn't have* and the verbs in brackets.

1 I'm not sure where Jess is, but she _____ home. She wasn't feeling well earlier on. (go)

2 You _____ Dave at the football match. He's away on holiday. (see)

3 Oh, no! Tanya knows about the surprise party. Someone _____ her. (tell)

4 I've missed my train. I _____ a taxi to the station instead of walking. (get)

5 It's been really hard to concentrate today. I _____ (stay) up late last night.

6 She should definitely be here by now. Her plane _____ . (delay)

7 I'm not sure why they didn't come. The postal service isn't very reliable so they _____ the invitation. (not receive)

8 There's no money in my bank account. I _____ so much on clothes last weekend. (spend)

Mark: ____ / 8

Use of English

9 Complete the second sentence so that it means the same as the first. Write up to five words in each gap. Sometimes more than one answer may be possible.

1 I advise you to apologise before it's too late.
You _____ before it's too late.

2 I'm sure my purse is at home. It isn't in my bag.
My purse isn't in my bag. It _____ at home.

3 It isn't necessary to dress up for the dinner. It's going to be quite informal.
It's quite an informal dinner. You _____ for it.

4 The use of mobile phones is prohibited in this hospital.
You _____ your mobile phone in this hospital.

5 It's impossible for me to help you move house next weekend. I'm sorry.
I'm afraid I won't _____ move house next weekend.

6 It's possible he didn't see you, so he didn't say hello.
He didn't say hello because he _____ you.

7 It was a really bad idea to wear jeans to the wedding.
I _____ jeans to the wedding.

8 I'm sure my sister didn't make this cake. She can't cook!
My sister _____ this cake. She can't cook!

9 Why didn't you tell me you were vegetarian? I've made a beef lasagne.
You _____ me you were vegetarian! I've made a beef lasagne.

10 It wasn't necessary for us to bring any towels, but we did because we didn't know.
We _____ any towels.

Mark: ____ / 10

Total: ____ / 60

I can ...

Read the statements. Think about your progress and tick one of the boxes.

★ = I need more practice.   ★★★ = No problem!

★★ = I sometimes find this difficult.

	★	★★	★★★
I can describe body language, gestures and movement.			
I can use modals to talk about present and future possibility.			
I can identify different types of listening text.			
I can use modal verbs to talk about past actions.			
I can recognise differences between American and British English.			
I can understand a review of an American novel.			
I can talk about a cultural event or festival.			
I can write a blog post.			

4 Holidays and tourism

Vocabulary

A Getting away from it all

I can describe types of holidays.

1 Put the words below in the correct column.

adventure holiday   backpacking   beach holiday
beach house   caravan   cruise   guest house   holiday home
self-catering apartment   surfing   tent
time-share apartment   volunteering   winter sports holiday

Holiday accommodation	Types of holidays

2 Match the holiday accommodation below with the sentences.

B&B   hotel   house swap   self-catering apartment
villa   youth hostel

1 'The website said it had four stars, but the room was really small and there wasn't any Wi-Fi. If you wanted to use the internet, you had to go and use some computers in the lobby!' _____

2 'We were really lucky because their flat was right in the centre of Rome. It also had a lovely balcony with views of the square. I think they were happy with ours because it's only fifteen minutes from Trafalgar Square on the underground.' _____

3 'Although it was on the coast, it also had a lovely swimming pool and a big terrace where we sat in the evenings. There were four bedrooms and enough room for all the family.' _____

4 'It was cheap, but we had to share a room with six other people who we didn't know. One guy spent the whole night talking in his sleep and kept me awake!' _____

5 'The room was fine and the breakfast was enormous. We didn't need to have lunch!' _____

6 'It seemed like a good idea at first because we could eat when we wanted, but we spent a lot of time shopping in supermarkets for food.' _____

3 🎧 **1.20** Listen to Alex and Jessica choosing a holiday. Underline the four types of holiday they mention. Which holiday do they choose to go on?

city break   cycling holiday   houseboat holiday   house swap
package holiday   volunteering holiday

4 🎧 **1.20** Listen again and complete the sentences with the adjectives below.

commercialised   crowded   dull   inaccessible   run-down
unspoilt

1 Jessica doesn't think anyone will want to come to their hometown because it is _____ .

2 Jessica doesn't like Alex's second suggestion because the holiday destination will be _____ with tourists and very _____ .

3 Alex doesn't like Jessica's suggestion because he thinks the accommodation will be _____ and the place _____ .

4 They finally decide to visit the west of Ireland, which is _____ .

5 Replace the underlined words with the adjectives below.

breathtaking   dingy   hospitable
remote   unique   vibrant

1 The view from the top of the mountain is <u>extremely beautiful</u>. _____

2 Our hotel room was <u>dark and dirty</u>. _____

3 The village is quite <u>far away</u>, but it's worth going there as it's so beautiful and unspoiled. _____

4 The people are really <u>friendly and helpful</u>. _____

5 New York is an incredibly <u>energetic and exciting</u> city. _____

6 This coastal town has a <u>special, unusual</u> atmosphere that will be different from anything you've experienced. _____

6 Complete the email with the words below.

adventure   batteries   easy   experiences   pamper
physically

> To: kate@email.com
>
> Hi Kate
>
> I'm on holiday! I decided to take it ¹_____ and ²_____ myself at a luxury hotel. However, after two days, I'm bored! I wish I had decided to be ³_____ active and find ⁴_____ somewhere! This hotel is great and I've recharged my ⁵_____ , but now I wish I could have new ⁶_____ !
> If only there were more things to do!
> Best wishes,
> Harry

7 Match 1–8 with a–h.

1 They say that travel
2 You need plenty of time to
3 We wanted to try
4 I like to hang
5 When you travel alone, you meet
6 We enjoyed
7 We like to eat
8 I really need to get

a out with my friends at the weekends.
b the local food, but we could only find fast-food restaurants!
c away from it all and relax.
d broadens your horizons.
e people from interesting places.
f out in good restaurants.
g see the sights in New York.
h the nightlife, but the beaches weren't very nice.

Future continuous, future perfect and future perfect continuous

I can use the future continuous and future perfect forms.

1 Choose the correct words to complete the sentences.

1 By the time I go on holiday, I'll **have saved** / **be saving** plenty of spending money.

2 Could you call me back in half an hour? I expect I'll **be finishing** / **have finished** lunch by then.

3 Tomorrow, we'll **be studying** / **have studied** Australia.

4 I won't **be playing** / **have played** in the football match this Saturday as I'll be on my way to Spain.

5 What will you **be doing** / **have done** at 7 p.m. tomorrow?

6 We still won't **have finished** / **be finishing** our exams by next Monday.

2 Correct the mistakes in the sentences. Tick the correct sentences.

1 Will you have cleaned your room by lunchtime? ☐

2 By the end of May, I'll be living here for ten years. ☐

3 It's hoped that scientists will have discovered a cure for cancer soon. ☐

4 How long will you be studying English for by the end of this year? ☐

5 They will have released the album by the end of May. ☐

6 I will be growing my hair for two years soon. ☐

3 Complete the text with the future continuous, future perfect, or future perfect continuous form of the verbs in brackets.

It started life above a pizza shop in the USA, but the world's most visited travel website, TripAdvisor,
¹_____ (run) for over fifteen years by the end of this month. This year, millions of us
²_____ (read) the online reviews and using them to help us plan our holidays. The most reviewed city is London – very soon, reviewers ³_____ (post) over two million reviews and ⁴_____ (give) the city's attractions a rating out of five 'bubbles'. Astonishingly, the website ⁵_____ (receive) reviews for so long that very soon, the total number of words published
⁶_____ (approach) 12,000 times the number of words in the complete works of Shakespeare!

4 Write the words in the correct order to form polite questions.

1 going / what / will / be / you / home / time / ?

_____

2 he / party / the / inviting / who / be / will / to / ?

_____

3 coming / when / of / be / out / will / hospital / she / ?

_____

4 be / will / leaving / teacher / year / why / next / our / ?

_____

5 seeing / you / tomorrow / be / will / Marco / ?

_____

6 match / will / the / be / in / you / who / supporting / ?

_____

Where ¹___ on your next holiday? Wherever it is, you're unlikely to stay in accommodation as old as the Hoshi Ryokan hotel and spa in Japan. Next month, it ²___ guests for over 1,300 years. The same family ³___ it for 46 generations, so the hotel ⁴___ as one of the world's oldest continuously operating businesses: visitors have been enjoying the traditional gardens and magnificent scenery for centuries. If you're tempted to stay, guests this year ⁵___ around US$190 per night, so ⁶___ for some time before you can afford to go!

5 Choose the correct options (a–c) to complete the text above.

1 a will you have stayed   b will you be staying
  c will you have been staying

2 a will have been welcoming   b will be welcoming
  c will have welcomed

3 a will be owning   b will have owned
  c will have been owning

4 a will have run   b will be running
  c will have been running

5 a will be paying   b will have been paying
  c will have paid

6 a you'll probably have been saving
  b you'll probably have saved
  c you'll probably be saving

6 Complete the mini-dialogues with the correct form of the verbs in brackets.

1 **A** Does Frank know about the party? Can I mention it to him?
  B Wait until this afternoon. I'll _____ (speak) to him by then.

2 **A** Have you heard from Mia recently?
  B No, but I _____ (meet) her tomorrow.

3 **A** Where shall we stop?
  B At the next town. We _____ (travel) for three hours by then.

4 **A** Are you going dancing tonight?
  B Probably not. My grandparents _____ (visit) later.

5 **A** Are you ready for Thursday's test?
  B I hope so. I _____ (revise) for a week by then!

Trip of a lifetime

I can identify the context of a conversation.

Revision: Student's Book page 45

1 Match 1–10 with a–j to make travel collocations.

1 get	a a local dish
2 go	b off the beaten track
3 taste	c the tent
4 put up	d a campfire
5 light	e away from it all
6 do	f with your bags
7 have	g a lovely view
8 help	h some volunteer work
9 travel	i rough
10 sleep	j light

2 Complete the text with travel collocations from exercise 1.

IF YOU ARE A TRAVELLER, NOT A TOURIST – IF YOU LIKE TO
¹_____ **RATHER THAN FOLLOW THE CROWDS –**
THEN COME TO ICELAND FOR A WHOLE NEW EXPERIENCE!

Iceland is wild and exciting and you can really forget about home and just ² _____ in this breathtaking environment. Stay in some of our lovely little hotels and you can ³ _____ of ice-capped mountains from your window. Then join us to go whale watching, or fishing in frozen lakes. You can ⁴ _____ on the lakeshore to cook your freshly caught fish and take a sleeping bag to sleep under the stars! Or you can ⁵ _____ in one of the many wonderful restaurants, if you prefer. Afterwards, you can relax outside in a volcanic hot tub!

3 🎧 **1.21 Read the Listening Strategy. Listen to four conversations and make notes on the topics below.**

a Where is each person?
1 _____ 3 _____
2 _____ 4 _____

b What kind of relationship is it?
1 _____ 3 _____
2 _____ 4 _____

c What is the approximate time of day of the conversation?
1 _____ 3 _____
2 _____ 4 _____

d What is the outcome of the conversation?
1 _____ 3 _____
2 _____ 4 _____

4 Add *just* in the correct place in the sentences.

1 I have a short time. _____
2 Could you close the door? _____
3 I got to the train in time. _____
4 It's amazing! _____
5 He has left. _____
6 We have to buy milk now. _____
7 This film's so funny! _____
8 Could you repeat your name? _____

5 Match the purpose of using *just* (a–d) with sentences 1–8 in exercise 4.

a for emphasis ___ ___
b to mean *only* ___ ___
c for politeness ___ ___
d to mean *close to the time* ___ ___

6 🎧 **1.22 Listen to the conversation. Are the sentences true (T) or false (F)?**

1 The conversation is happening in a restaurant. ☐
2 John reacts to both of Ella's suggestions with decisiveness. ☐
3 Ella would prefer to spend the day sightseeing. ☐
4 John is worried the bus might be too hot. ☐
5 Ella's attitude is that you should make the most of a trip away. ☐

Listening Strategy
Listen carefully for who the speakers are and where they might be. This will help you to identify the context of the conversation, and also to find out what the speakers' purpose is.

4D Grammar
Future time clauses
I can use future time clauses.

1 Choose the correct options (a–c) to complete the text.

If you're thinking of volunteering abroad, why not join us on one of our conservation trips to Costa Rica this year? We take care of all your travel arrangements, so as soon as ¹___ , one of our group leaders will meet you at the airport. Then, once ²___ time to relax, and after ³___ everyone else in the group, we take you on the four-hour bus journey to the coast. You'll be working in the Tortuguero National Park on one of our conservation projects – but when ⁴___ , there's plenty of time to enjoy the beautiful beaches, and while ⁵___ here you could even learn a new language. We're sure that by the time ⁶___ you'll have had an amazing experience!

1	a you're arriving	b you arrive	c you'll be arriving
2	a you've had	b you're having	c you'll be having
3	a you'll have met	b you've met	c you'll be meeting
4	a you don't work	b you aren't working	c you haven't worked
5	a you're staying	b you'll be staying	c you'll have stayed
6	a you'll have left	b you'll be leaving	c you leave

2 Complete the text with the correct form of the verbs in brackets.

Hi Otto

I can't wait to see you – I can't believe that by the time I ¹_____ (see) you, I ²_____ (be) France for a month! As soon as you ³_____ (arrive), we'll plan where to go, but can you bring a sleeping bag in case we ⁴_____ (decide) to go camping? Tomorrow, I ⁵_____ (visit) my cousins in Paris, so it's a shame we'll have to wait until Saturday to meet, but I should be there the minute your train ⁶_____ (get) in. Just think: this time on Saturday, we ⁷_____ (talk) to each other face to face! Lots of love until then.

Sam

3 Choose the best verb form to complete the first conditional sentences.

1 If they go to Amsterdam, **they will have / they are having** a great time.
2 If you're buying a new outfit for the party, **I get / I'm getting** one too.
3 If you get out of school before me, **wait / you'll wait** for me at the bus stop.
4 If we don't hurry up, we **won't be finishing / won't have finished** this exercise by the end of the lesson.
5 If he gets good grades, my brother **goes / will go** to university.
6 If this DVD's any good, I'll **lend / have lent** it to you.

4 Choose the answer that makes most sense. Sometimes both answers are possible.

1 I'll let you know **as soon as / in case** I've booked my ticket.
2 If it stays hot, the clothes will have dried **the minute / by the time** we leave.
3 My parents will let me go camping **on condition that / once** I phone every day.
4 **By the time / When** she lands in New York, she'll have been travelling for two days.
5 **If / Unless** you need anything, just ask at reception.
6 Take a book **in case / on condition that** you get bored on the flight.

5 Complete the second sentence so that it means the same as the first.

1 I won't take suncream unless you do.
   If you don't _____ either.
2 It may rain later, so take an umbrella.
   Take an umbrella in _____ .
3 I'll finish packing and then I'll call a cab.
   After _____ call a cab.
4 You won't hear from me again until I'm in London.
   By _____ me again, I'll be in London.
5 He can't go unless he finds his passport soon.
   If _____ soon, he won't be able to go.
6 We can't share a room if you snore!
   We can share a room on condition
   _____ !

Adverbs and adverbial phrases
I can use adverbs and adverbial phrases.

1 Complete the sentences with the words below.

early friendly monthly motherly weekly yearly

1 We love going camping and try to go _____ – usually in September.
2 Lessons will finish _____ today for the parents' meeting.
3 'Do you go shopping every week?' 'No, we just do one big shop _____.'
4 He gestured in a _____ way and invited us over.
5 She hugged the crying child in a _____ way.
6 I see Nina _____ when we play tennis on Saturdays.

2 Write the words in the correct order to make sentences.

1 my / monthly / renew / membership / I / gym
_____

2 a / way / smiled / lovely / she / in / really
_____

3 band / town / my / in / plays / brother's / fortnightly
_____

4 a / the / spoke / way / in / man / cowardly
_____

5 crashed / driving / when / she / fast / was / too / she
_____

6 diving / can / to / he / annually / go / afford / ?
_____

3 Choose the correct adverb (a or b) to complete the sentences.

1 The dentist asked her to open her mouth ___ .
   a wide   b widely
2 Despite watching ___ , I don't know how the magician did that!
   a closely   b close
3 I haven't seen you ___ – is everything ok?
   a late   b lately
4 The next train goes ___ to London without stopping.
   a direct   b directly
5 Shall we sit ___ to the door so we can leave quietly?
   a close   b closely
6 We'll be there in ___ half an hour.
   a roughly   b rough

VOCAB BOOST!

When you come across adverbs which have two forms, e.g. *deep / deeply*, write down example sentences to show the different meanings and to help you remember them.

Don't swim too far out; the water's really deep.
I'm deeply sorry for upsetting you.

4 Read the *Vocab boost!* box and complete the pairs of sentences with the correct form of the adverbs below.

close flat free hard late near

1 a They're identical twins; you can _____ tell them apart.
   b It started to rain _____ just as we left the house.
2 a This DVD came _____ with my magazine.
   b You can speak _____ here – we're all good friends.
3 a I love cricket so I've been following the match _____ .
   b We couldn't get _____ enough to ask for his autograph.
4 a All the students _____ denied cheating.
   b She has a strong voice but a rather _____ tone.
5 a I _____ forgot to pack my swimming costume!
   b It's November and Christmas is getting _____ .
6 a Don't go to bed _____ tonight; remember that we've got an early start tomorrow.
   b Katya hasn't been well _____ so she won't be at school.

5 Complete the text with the words below.

closely hardly lately lively
nearly rough widely

In *Down and Out in Paris and London* (1933), author George Orwell writes about the poverty in the two cities, describing in a ¹_____ way his experience of mixing with the very poor. After living in Paris for ²_____ two years, Orwell fell seriously ill and had all his money stolen. He then returned to London, sleeping ³_____ and living ⁴_____ with tramps. His book was ⁵_____ praised at the time for its honest study, but it seems that some things have ⁶_____ changed more than eighty years on. Parts of the cities have become very rich ⁷_____ , but the problems of unemployment and homelessness still exist.

6 Choose the correct words (a–d) to complete the sentences.

1 It's so dark that I can ___ see anything.
   a hard   b hardly   c harder   d hardest
2 The doctor gave me tablets that I must take ___ .
   a by day   b daily   c a day   d the day
3 Everyone was ___ upset to hear the news.
   a deep   b deeply   c in a deep way   d deep in
4 We shouldn't leave home ___ tomorrow if we want to catch the train.
   a late   b lately   c later   d latest
5 Do you live ___ your grandparents?
   a near   b nearby   c nearly   d by near
6 The cat lay ___ on the cold floor to cool down.
   a flat   b flatter   c flatly   d in a flat way

Globetrotters

I can understand a text about adventure holidays.

Revision: Student's Book page 48

1 Complete the email with the correct form of the verbs below.

come   get (x2)   go   pull   set   stop   take

To: frank@email.com

Hi Frank

We went to Petra yesterday. We ¹_____ off from Amman, the capital, very early in the morning. During the coach journey, we ²_____ up at a small town for a break. We finally arrived at Petra and it was amazing! Andy ³_____ off to climb the hills to get a better view of the city. I saw quite a few people ⁴_____ around on camels, but I didn't fancy exploring the place in this way! I ⁵_____ across some local people selling beautiful handmade souvenirs and bought a few.

Andy wanted to ⁶_____ over in a local hotel to ⁷_____ in more of the monuments the next day, but I wanted to ⁸_____ back to the capital so we could visit that too. There's so much to see in Jordan! More news tomorrow!

Bye for now!

Amy

2 Read the texts. Are the sentences true (T) or false (F)?

1 In the past, adventure holidays were something that only the well-off could afford to do. ☐
2 The crocodiles at Crocosaurus swim inside a glass cage that is lowered into the water. ☐
3 The spa in Israel is overcrowded. ☐
4 The visitors lie on their backs on the massage table. ☐
5 You have to walk along the 'Changong Zhando' in order to get to the top of Mount Haushan. ☐
6 The 'Changong Zhando' is through two mountains. ☐

Reading Strategy

When you have to match statements or questions with different texts, you must remember that some of the topics or key words from the task may appear in several of the texts. Study each text carefully to decide which of the statements or questions matches it most closely.

3 Read the Reading Strategy. Match texts A–C with questions 1–6 below. Each text may be matched with more than one question.

Which text mentions ...
1 a route that visitors have to take? ☐
2 unexpected sensations? ☐
3 the age of the facilities? ☐
4 the chance to reduce stress? ☐
5 protective equipment? ☐
6 losing weight? ☐

Living dangerously!

These days, having adventure holidays is no longer for the privileged few. If you're looking for new experiences, we've got some incredible suggestions for you!

A Crocosaurus Cove, Australia

If you think adventure is synonymous with wild animals, then you should try the Cage of Death at Crocosaurus Cove in Darwin, Australia, where you can swim with crocodiles for fifteen minutes! Visitors climb into a cage made of glass walls that are four centimetres thick and are then lowered into a pool where an enormous 'croc' (six metres long and weighing eight hundred kilos) is waiting! It's an unforgettable experience and you'll be telling your friends about it for years to come.

B Talmei Elazar, Israel

A relaxing massage at a spa is the perfect way to chill out and escape the overcrowded tourist zones. However, this spa in northern Israel employs unusual staff members to give the massages: snakes! The owner, Ada Barack, asks clients to lie on the massage table and then drops six snakes onto their backs! Visitors say they expect the snakes to feel wet, but in fact they are cool, dry and smooth. You may feel a little tense at the beginning, but you'll be leaving the spa feeling more relaxed than you have in a long time!

C Mount Haushan, China

Seeing the sights at the top of Mount Haushan in China is not for people who don't like heights! After climbing the hundreds of steep steps that are cut into the rock, visitors have to walk along the 'Changong Zhando'. This is the name given to the terrifying walk along two narrow pieces of wood on the side of the mountain which are only forty centimetres wide. There is just a seven-hundred-year-old chain handrail fixed into the rock to stop you from falling over two thousand metres to your death! You'll have lost a few kilos through exercise and worry by the time you reach the top!

Interview and stimulus-based discussion
I can discuss a topic and select and justify my choice from a range of options.

1 When you plan travelling for leisure, what is the most important consideration for you before you make your choice? Why? Tell your partner. Use the ideas below to help you.

cost   interest   location   safety   time   your own idea

2 Read the task below. Decide which advert is more appealing to you. Think of four reasons.

> You are planning a holiday abroad. Read the adverts below. Which trip appeals to you more? Say why and explain why you are rejecting the other option.

A ONLY £20 FOR STUDENTS.
TRAVEL THE CANALS FOR A COUPLE OF HOURS.

B Private day trips
Have lunch in the old port.
Only £30 for students.

3 🎧 1.23 Read the Speaking Strategy below. Listen to a student doing the task. Tick the topics she mentions. Were any of her reasons the same as yours?

comfort ☐   boredom ☐   convenience ☐
cost ☐   interest ☐   length of trip ☐
safety ☐   speed ☐   sea sickness ☐

Speaking Strategy
When you explain which item you are choosing, try to give a number of different reasons for your choice. When you are saying why you reject the other options, try again to give more than one reason. Do not simply give opposite reasons. Try to come up with different arguments.

4 🎧 1.23 Listen again. Tick the phrases the student uses.
1 I think I'll choose … mainly because … ☐
2 I'm opting for … and that's because … ☐
3 The best option would be the … because … ☐
4 I wouldn't pick the … for the reason that … ☐
5 I wouldn't go for the … basically because … ☐
6 The (other) reason why I'm (not) choosing the … is that … ☐

5 Read the task and look at the photos below. Compare the options. Prepare the reasons for your choice under the headings (1–4) below.

> You are on holiday abroad. Which of these activities would you choose and why? Say why you are rejecting the other option.

A Get ready for your first paragliding experience!
No experience necessary – just a head for heights!
Only £25 for students.

B PARAGLIDING FOR ADVENTURE LOVERS
ONLY £50 FOR STUDENTS.

1 interest for you

2 location

3 cost

4 time required

6 Now do the task using your notes from exercise 5.

4H

A letter of complaint

I can write a formal letter of complaint.

Preparation

1 Rewrite the sentences in more formal language. Use the correct form of the words in brackets.

1 I got the booking information from you. (receive)

_____

2 Your company didn't say sorry. (offer / no apology)

_____

3 I really think you are to blame. (feel strongly / at fault)

_____

4 I think your online system should be looked at. (believe / review)

_____

5 I don't want other people to have the same problems that I had. (be inconvenienced / I was)

_____

6 Further problems will happen. (arise)

_____

2 Read the task and the letter below. What three things does the writer suggest?

You had a very poor train journey recently. You were rather dissatisfied with the experience. Write a letter to the train company saying why you are unhappy and suggest ways in which the service could be improved.

Dear Sir or Madam

I am writing to complain about my train journey with Great Eastern on Sunday 20 July.

I booked a return ticket, reserved seats through your website and received confirmation of the booking. However, when I boarded the train, my seat was already occupied by someone with the same reservation. I therefore had to stand for 45 minutes. To make matters worse, there was a delay in the departure of the train, but we were given no information about this. We were held up for 35 minutes, which resulted in me missing my connection and losing my second seat reservation. I therefore waited for the next train. However, the air conditioning was not functioning in this train, and it was a very hot three-hour journey. There was no apology at any point.

I feel strongly that I deserve compensation for this deeply unsatisfactory journey. Firstly, I suggest that your online booking system be reviewed, as there are clearly problems. Secondly, there should be more information and help for passengers when problems occur. Finally, I request that there be bottled water available in extremely hot conditions.

I am applying for a refund for my journey. I look forward to hearing from you.

Yours faithfully

Simon Harding

Writing Strategy

When you write a formal letter:

1 Divide your letter into paragraphs.

2 In the introduction, explain why you are writing. At the end, tell the reader what you would like them to do.

3 Use formal language and avoid contractions and abbreviations.

4 Use the appropriate phrases to start and finish your letter, depending on whether you know the recipient by name.

Dear Sir or Madam → Yours faithfully

Dear Mr Black / Ms White, etc. → Yours sincerely

3 Find two examples of the subjunctive form in the letter.

4 Rewrite the requests and demands using the subjunctive and the words in brackets.

1 I think you should review the booking procedure. (suggest)

_____

2 I think you should announce delays. (recommend)

_____

3 I think you should delay your decision. (propose)

_____

4 I want my ticket to be refunded. (demand)

_____

Writing Guide

On a recent holiday, you and a group of friends went on a sightseeing bus tour. You were very dissatisfied with the experience. Write a letter to the company saying why you are unhappy and suggest ways in which the tour might be improved.

5 Read the task above and make notes about what you will complain about. Use the ideas below or your own ideas.

itinerary missed out an important place
tour didn't run on time
tour guide was unenthusiastic / too quiet
no toilet on the bus

6 Write your letter of complaint.

CHECK YOUR WORK

Have you …

☐ organised your letter in paragraphs?

☐ started and finished the letter appropriately?

☐ avoided contractions and informal language?

Review Unit 4

Vocabulary

1 Use a word from A and a word from B to make compound nouns. Then complete the sentences.

A back camp camper city guest package self-catering youth

B apartment break holiday hostel house packing site van

1 When my friends were in New Zealand, they hired a _____ to travel around South Island.
2 The price of our _____ included the flight, the hotel and some of the excursions.
3 The _____ they chose had a field for caravans as well as several for tents.
4 My parents have gone on a _____ to Rome to celebrate their wedding anniversary.
5 The _____ we stayed at only had six rooms, but it was very comfortable and the owners were nice.
6 We prefer to do our own cooking, so we tend to rent a _____ when we go away.
7 _____ is the cheapest way to see a country.
8 There were ten people to a dormitory in the _____ we slept in.

Mark: ___ / 8

2 Replace the underlined words with the synonyms below.

dingy overcrowded remote run-down unspoilt vibrant

1 Rio de Janeiro is at its most <u>exciting</u> at carnival time. _____
2 Some of Britain's beach resorts are rather <u>neglected</u>. _____
3 The <u>isolated</u> village we stayed in was over 30 km from the nearest big town. _____
4 Many of the beaches in Menorca are completely <u>natural</u>. _____
5 It's best to avoid the city centre at weekends because the shops are <u>full of people</u>. _____
6 They gave us a <u>dark and dirty</u> room at the back of the hotel, so we asked if we could change. _____

Mark: ___ / 6

3 Complete the questions with travel collocations. Use one or two words.

1 Would you _____ a campfire on the beach?
2 Can you _____ a tent and take it down again on your own?
3 Do you _____ light when you go on holiday or do you take a lot of luggage?
4 Where do you go when you want to _____ from it all?

5 Do you ever _____ the beaten track?
6 Would you ever _____ rough if you didn't have anywhere to stay?

Mark: ___ / 6

Word Skills

4 Complete the sentences with the correct adverb form of the adjectives in brackets.

1 It took us _____ half an hour to get there. (rough)
2 We booked the hotel _____ to ensure that we got a nice room. (early)
3 Try _____ not to look like a tourist when you're alone in a foreign country. (hard)
4 I looked at the bill _____ to make sure it was correct. (close)
5 The weather has been terrible _____ . I hope it improves for our holiday. (late)
6 We're going to have to decide where to go _____ soon, or everything will be booked up. (pretty)

Mark: ___ / 6

5 Complete the mini-dialogues with the phrasal verbs below.

get around   get back   go off   pull up   set off   stop over

1 **A** What time are you leaving in the morning?
  B We're going to _____ at 6.30 a.m.
2 **A** Did you walk everywhere in London?
  B No, we used the tourist bus to _____ .
3 **A** What time does your plane land?
  B At 6.00; we should _____ to the house around 8.00.
4 **A** Have you got a direct flight?
  B No, it's going to _____ in Doha on the way.
5 **A** Did you go on holiday with your parents?
  B Yes, but I could _____ and do my own thing.
6 **A** Where shall I park?
  B Just _____ outside the hotel for now.

Mark: ___ / 6

6 Complete the sentences with the phrases below.

I'm opting   I think   I wouldn't   I wouldn't pick
The best option   The reason why

1 _____ for an elderly couple would be a cruise, because they wouldn't have to walk very far.
2 _____ the holiday camp for the reason that it would be too noisy.
3 _____ for the B&B, and that's because they tend to be cheaper.
4 _____ I'm not choosing the houseboat is that it might be very cramped.

5 _____ go for the cycling holiday, basically because I haven't got a bike.

6 _____ I'll choose the winter sports holiday, mainly because I love skiing.

Mark: ___ / 6

Grammar

7 Choose the correct answers (a–c).

1 Holly's flight from Paris to San Francisco leaves at 9 a.m. At 6 p.m., she ___ for nine hours.
   a will have flown   b will be flying
   c will have been flying

2 I'm doing an online Spanish course before I go to Spain. I hope I ___ enough by the time I go.
   a will have learned   b will be learning
   c will have been learning

3 My dad leaves work at 6.30 p.m. and doesn't get home until 7.15 p.m. I can't call him now because he ___ .
   a will have driven   b will be driving
   c will have been driving

4 We usually have dinner at 6.00. I'm sure we ___ by 7.00 so you can call me then.
   a will have finished   b will be finishing
   c will have been finishing

5 I've been saving £150 a month since September. By the end of the year, I ___ £600.
   a will have saved   b will be saving
   c will have been saving

6 The coach to Edinburgh leaves at 11 a.m. and takes nine and a half hours. At 6 p.m., we ___ on the coach.
   a will have sat   b will be sitting
   c will have been sitting

Mark: ___ / 6

8 Complete the sentences with the correct form of the verbs in brackets.

1 I won't go to the beach tomorrow if it _____ . (rain)

2 Tony's going to pack his bags before he _____ to bed. (go)

3 I'll be able to tell you what time I'm leaving once I _____ the time of my flight. (check)

4 We'll be staying with my aunt when we _____ in Vancouver. (be)

5 Can you call me after you _____ dinner? (have)

6 I'm not going to tell you about my trip until I can see that you _____ to me. (listen)

Mark: ___ / 6

Use of English

9 Complete the text with one word in each gap.

Potential space travellers will ¹_____ watching the progress of space tourism company Virgin Galactic closely after its spacecraft broke into pieces during a test flight. Since the accident, several customers who had booked a flight have cancelled in ²_____ the trip never happens. The company is now building a replacement spaceship, and commercial operations will begin once it ³_____ been fully tested. Only then ⁴_____ the first passengers be invited to Spaceport America. But they will only be allowed to fly on ⁵_____ that they pass rigorous medical checks. Those declared fit to fly will ⁶_____ to do a training course in preparation for the launch. Three days will have passed ⁷_____ the time they finally take off. During the flight, they will have a lovely ⁸_____ of the Earth from space, and at the furthest point, they will experience floating in zero gravity ⁹_____ six minutes. When they get ¹⁰_____ to the spaceport, they will join their family and friends to celebrate having become astronauts.

Mark: ___ / 10

Total: ___ / 60

I can ...

Read the statements. Think about your progress and tick one of the boxes.

★ = I need more practice.   ★★★ = No problem!

★★ = I sometimes find this difficult.

	★	★★	★★★
I can describe types of holidays.			
I can use future continuous and future perfect forms.			
I can identify the context of a conversation.			
I can use future time clauses.			
I can use adverbs and adverbial phrases.			
I can understand a text about adventure holidays.			
I can discuss a topic and select and justify my choice from a range of options.			
I can write a formal letter of complaint.			

Reading

1 Read the text and choose the correct answers (A, B, C, or D).

The rise of Airbnb

In 2007, design graduates, Joe Gebbie and Brian Chesky, were struggling to pay the rent for their San Francisco apartment. When they heard that there was a conference coming to town and there were no hotel rooms available, they came up with the idea of putting their living room floor up for rent. The next day, they created the website airbedandbreakfast.com where they advertised three airbeds in their home at $80 each a night, breakfast included. Only six days later, they had three guests sleeping on their floor. They knew immediately that this was the start of something big.

Being budding entrepreneurs, the pair decided to take their idea further. They enlisted Gebbie's former flatmate, Nathan Blecharczyk, a computer science graduate, to develop their website. Their idea was to target conferences and festivals across the USA, getting local people to list their rooms and travellers to book them. The new website was completed just in time for the 2008 Democratic National Convention in Denver, at which Barack Obama was due to speak in front of 80,000 people. Within a week, they had 800 listings, an achievement which dealt in part with the shortage of hotel rooms, but did not solve their financial problems, as the site was not making any money.

The team decided that they would have to handle payment for the bookings if they were to make their venture financially viable. They began to charge three per cent to the host and between six and twelve per cent to the traveller, depending on the price of the booking. Meanwhile, investors had started showing interest in the company. By April 2009, Gebbie, Chesky and Blecharcyzk were making enough money to cover their living expenses. When larger investments began to arrive, they moved the company out of their flat into a new state-of-the-art office and hired more staff.

Airbnb hit one million bookings in January 2011, and since then it has gone from strength to strength. It hasn't been plain sailing, however. When one host complained on her blog later that year that her house had been trashed by an Airbnb renter, the story was reported internationally in the press. The company responded by announcing that in future hosts would be insured and there would be a 24/7 manned helpline to deal with any complaints. A month later, another victim of vandalism was compensated immediately and has gone on to rent out his apartment through the website again. Thanks to quick thinking like this, the company now has over 1.5 million listings in 34,000 cities in 190 countries, and is rumoured to be worth around $20 billion.

1 Gebbie and Chesky decided to rent out floor space because
  A they wanted to attract people to a conference in their area.
  B they needed money to redecorate the living room.
  C there weren't any hotels near their local conference centre.
  D there was a temporary need for accommodation in the city.

2 The new website designed by Nathan Blecharczyk enabled Gebbie and Chesky to
  A accommodate most of the guests at a Denver convention.
  B make a huge profit as soon as it was launched.
  C rent out properties nationally.
  D put travellers in touch with hosts abroad.

3 When booking a room with Airbnb,
  A it is only the guest who pays.
  B both the guest and the host have to pay.
  C the guest pays a fixed percentage of the price.
  D the guest and the host share the cost equally.

4 Until April 2009, Gebbie and Chesky were running the business from
  A a brand new building.
  B a friend's house.
  C their own home.
  D a flat on Wall Street.

5 In paragraph four, the writer mentions the two acts of vandalism
  A to illustrate the speed with which the company reacts to problems.
  B to highlight how irresponsible some of the travellers are.
  C to emphasise the different treatment that some hosts receive.
  D to show how quick the media are to criticise the company.

Listening

2 Read the Strategy and find phrases in the questions in exercise 3 that could be paraphrased with the phrases below.

1 ask for help _____
2 wasn't getting on with _____
3 head home earlier than planned _____
4 didn't bother taking _____
5 gave up using _____

3 🎧 **1.24** You will hear four speakers talking about their experiences of camping. Match questions A–E with speakers 1–4. There is one extra question.

Which speaker …

A didn't feel comfortable with the people they were with?

B wasn't able to use all of the facilities they were provided with?

C omitted to pack something essential for the trip?

D had to call for assistance in the middle of the night?

E was forced to cut their holiday short?

Speaker 1: ___   Speaker 3: ___

Speaker 2: ___   Speaker 4: ___

Use of English

> **Strategy**
>
> Read the instructions carefully so that you know how many words to write in the gap. Make sure that the second sentence expresses exactly the same meaning as the first one and that you have not added any new ideas or left anything out. Use the key word exactly as it is written and do not change it in any way.

4 Read the Strategy. Read the sentence and choose the correct transformation, a, b, c, or d. Why are the other sentences wrong?

I've never stayed in such a bad hotel. (ever)

a That's the first hotel I've ever stayed in.

b That's the worst hotel I've ever stayed in.

c That's the bad hotel everyone stayed in.

d That's the very bad hotel I've ever stayed in.

5 Complete the second sentence so that it means the same as the first. Use between two and five words, including the word in brackets. Do not change the word in brackets.

1 A package holiday is nowhere near as expensive as a cruise. (far)
A cruise is _____ a package holiday.

2 I knew it was a bad idea for us to leave home so late. (have)
We _____ so late.

3 It's going to take me half an hour to make lunch. (will)
In half an hour, _____ lunch.

4 If they don't give us another room, we're changing hotels. (unless)
We're changing hotels _____ _____ another room.

5 Sorry, but I don't want to go swimming today. (rather)
Sorry, but _____ swimming today.

6 I expect you were sad to leave after having such a good time. (must)
You _____ to leave after having such a good time.

Speaking

> **Strategy**
>
> In a photo comparison task, you may be asked to talk about the advantages and disadvantages of an activity or a situation.

6 Look at the two photos below that show different places to stay. Compare the photos using the points below.

- location
- facilities
- cost
- activities

Writing

> **Strategy**
>
> Learn how to use fixed expressions and phrases that are typical of formal letters, such as letters of complaint.

7 Read the Strategy. Then replace the underlined phrases with the more formal phrases below.

action you intend to take   express strong dissatisfaction   in the circumstances   misleading   refund in full   regret to inform you

1 I am writing to <u>say that I am not satisfied</u> with the trip organised by your travel agency. _____

2 I <u>am sorry to say to you</u> that the information given by your sales assistant was <u>not true</u>. _____

3 <u>In this situation</u>, I feel that it would be appropriate for you to <u>give me back the whole of the cost of</u> our hotel stay.
_____ _____

4 Please let me know as soon as possible what <u>you plan to do</u>. _____

8 Read the task below and write your letter.

You have just come back from a class trip. Unfortunately, the trip did not meet your expectations. Write a letter to the organiser of the trip in which you say why you were dissatisfied with the programme and transport and suggest ways in which the agency could avoid similar problems in the future.

5 Relationships

Vocabulary

A Relating to people
I can talk about relationships and describe behaviour.

1 Complete the sentences with the words below.

close   common   eye   sorry   wary   wavelength

1 I don't really understand Kevin or his jokes. We really aren't on the same _____ .
2 Sara feels _____ for me for failing my exam, but it was my own fault.
3 We've got a lot in _____ with each other and we share quite a few interests.
4 My mother doesn't see _____ to eye with me about my plans for the weekend.
5 Although Jack has moved to London, we are still very _____ and are in contact every day.
6 I'm a bit _____ of giving my email address to people online that I don't know.

2 Replace the underlined words with the correct form of the verbs below.

adore   envy   look down on   look up to   respect   trust

1 We should <u>treat</u> the environment <u>carefully</u> and not pollute it. _____
2 Andy <u>thinks very highly of</u> his big brother Tom and wants to be just like him. _____
3 Some of his friends <u>are jealous of</u> the success that he has had. _____
4 My sister warned me not to <u>have confidence in</u> him. _____
5 She's afraid they <u>think they are better than</u> her because she doesn't have a job. _____
6 They have one son and they <u>really love</u> him. _____

3 🎧1.25 Listen and choose the correct answer (a–c).

1 The man in dialogue 1 suggests that he and Eva ___ .
  a are very close to each other   b adore each other
  c have nothing in common with each other
2 The woman in the second dialogue ___ her friend's family.
  a looks down on   b feels sorry for   c adores
3 The two people in dialogue 3 ___ the man they see.
  a are wary of   b are on the same wavelength as
  c respect
4 How does the girl in dialogue 4 feel about her brother?
  a She envies him.   b She looks up to him.
  c She despises him.
5 The girl in dialogue 5 feels confident that her friend ___ Amy.
  a can trust   b admires   c has a lot in common with
6 What problem do the two speakers in dialogue 6 have with Jack?
  a They have nothing in common with him.
  b They don't see eye to eye with him.
  c They are wary of him.

4 Complete the sentences with the prepositions below.

about (x3)   for (x2)   on

1 I was complimented _____ my winning entry for the poetry competition by the head teacher.
2 My dad is always being teased _____ his terrible cooking.
3 We were warned _____ the dangers of cycling at night.
4 Sam was told off _____ not taking his medicine.
5 The whole class might be lectured _____ behaving well when in public places.
6 We've all been praised _____ our performance in the play.

5 Match the verbs below with the situations.

flatter   insult   nag   praise   warn

1 'That's a fantastic piece of work, Lily. Well done!' _____
2 'I really like your new suit. You look great in it!' _____
3 'You are a complete idiot, aren't you?' _____
4 'Don't jump into the sea from the rocks. It's extremely dangerous!' _____
5 'Oh, please, please, please let me stay out late on Friday night. I promise that if you do, I'll ...' _____

6 Complete the text with the correct form of the verbs below.

compliment   nag   praise   tease   tell   warn

Well, it's been a bit of a strange day. My mum [1]_____ me off this morning for arriving home late last night, but then she [2]_____ me for my good marks in the test! On the bus to school, my best mate Harry kept [3]_____ me about lending him my mountain bike. He went on and on about it for the whole journey! Once at school, everyone made jokes and [4]_____ me about my new haircut. Well, everyone except for Chloe! She [5]_____ me on my 'stylish' hair and said it looked great! But then I realised that I'd left my English homework at home. My English teacher [6]_____ me not to forget my homework again and gave me extra work as a punishment!

1 Choose the correct answers (a–c) to complete the text.

We ¹___ expect our family or friends to turn against us and there can ²___ be a worse betrayal than one committed by a best friend. ³___ in literature has this been more powerfully expressed than by Shakespeare in his play *Julius Caesar*. ⁴___ Caesar sees his best friend Brutus among his murderers does he realise the extent of the betrayal against him. ⁵___ has Brutus stabbed him than Caesar falls to his death, speaking the famous line 'Et tu, Brute?', meaning 'And you, Brutus?' This is now a phrase often used to express sadness and surprise when you are let down by someone considered to be a trusted friend. Perhaps, like Caesar, it's ⁶___ we are let down badly by a good friend that we appreciate how devastating a betrayal can be.

1 a nowhere   b never   c no sooner
2 a hardly   b not until   c only if
3 a Not only   b In no way   c Nowhere
4 a At no time   b Only when   c Rarely
5 a No sooner   b Only once   c Under no circumstances
6 a not only   b hardly   c not until

2 Write the words in brackets in the correct order to complete the sentences.

1 Rarely (so / she / felt / unhappy / had).
_____

2 Nowhere (find / will / you / a / friend / better).
_____

3 Only (argued / have / ever / once / we).
_____

4 In no (did / to / upset / I / anyone / way / mean)!
_____

5 At (should / lies / tell / time / no / you).
_____

6 Under (can / him / no / you / circumstances / trust).
_____

7 Not (we / will / get / results / Friday / until / our).
_____

3 Match the sentence halves.

1 She was sorry   a split up with Nick?
2 Do you regret   b not to keep his promise.
3 Wouldn't it be sensible   c to go to bed early?
4 Hasn't she   d not to lose her friendship.
5 Weren't you   e at the café yesterday?
6 He is certain   f not inviting Jane?
7 He'll be lucky   g not to see him at the club.

4 Complete the dialogue with one word in each gap. Use negative structures.

Ada   Hi, Jan! ¹_____ you go out with Sara last night?

Jan   Yes, we went out for a pizza.

Ada   I was really sorry ²_____ to be able to join you. Did you have a good time?

Jan   Not really, no. No sooner ³_____ we arrived ⁴_____ we had a row!

Ada   Oh, that's not good.

Jan   I know. And not ⁵_____ that, but she isn't speaking to me now.

Ada   ⁶_____ it be a good idea to phone her and apologise?

Jan   Probably – I regret not ⁷_____ to her at the time, but I was too angry.

Ada   Well, under ⁸_____ circumstances should you forget to say sorry!

5 Complete the second sentence so that it means the same as the first. Write up to five words in each sentence.

1 We mustn't under any circumstances lose this key.
   Under _____ lose this key.

2 This band isn't at all special.
   In _____ at all special.

3 I regretted going as soon as I got there.
   No sooner _____ I regretted going.

4 My friends haven't judged me at any time.
   At no _____ judged me.

5 Bill wished he'd kept his news a secret.
   Bill regretted _____ a secret.

6 It was fortunate that we didn't get lost.
   We were lucky _____ .

7 I'm sure Jerry went into town last night.
   _____ town last night?

8 I can't make a decision until I've spoken to Pat.
   Not _____ Pat can I make a decision.

Sibling rivalry

I can understand a discussion about sibling rivalry.

Listening Strategy

Remember that spoken English can sound quite different from written language. In fast speech, fluent speakers often shorten or omit certain elements. It is possible to train yourself to understand fast speech. You do not need to imitate fast speakers, but focus on trying to understand what they are talking about.

1 🎧 **1.26** **Read the Listening Strategy. Listen to a student talking about his sister. Answer the questions.**

1 What was Ella's behaviour like?

_____

2 What kind of child was the speaker?

_____

3 What did people use to say to the speaker?

_____

4 How did the speaker feel about his sister when they were young?

_____

5 When did their relationship improve?

_____

2 Match the features of fast speech (a–c) with examples 1–3.

a *Tell everybody* sounds like *Tell leverybody.* ☐
b *That's my ...* sounds like *Thas my ...* ☐
c *So early* sounds like *so wearly*; *my uncle* sounds like *my yuncle* ☐

1 Consonants are sometimes inserted between two vowel sounds.
2 Consonant sounds at the end of words run into a following vowel sound.
3 Sounds, usually consonants, sometimes disappear.

3 🎧 **1.27** **Listen to the sentences from the text. Write down one or two features of fast speech that you hear in each.**

1 My sister was born with big, blue eyes ...

_____

2 She looked like an angel.

_____

3 This was not good news for me.

_____

4 Sometimes I pushed her away.

_____

5 Later, when I got better at school ...

_____

6 Now I think she's great too.

_____

4 🎧 **1.27** **Listen again and repeat. Try to copy the pronunciation.**

5 🎧 **1.28** **Listen to two dialogues and a monologue. Choose the correct answer (a–c).**

1 How does the first dialogue end?
   a The speakers refuse to listen to each other's point of view.
   b The speakers eventually come to an acknowledgment of each other's viewpoints.
   c The speakers decide that the disagreement can't be resolved.

2 What caused the speaker of the monologue to feel happier during her childhood?
   a Her parents had triplets.
   b A relative moved in with them.
   c Her brothers spent more time playing with her.

3 In the second dialogue, what do Linda and Cathy tell the interviewer?
   a How their parents' divorce affected them emotionally.
   b How Cathy continually annoyed Linda.
   c What the main cause of problems between them was.

6 🎧 **1.29** **Listen and write the sentences from the listening.**

1 _____

2 _____

3 _____

4 _____

5 _____

6 _____

7 🎧 **1.29** **How are the sentences in exercise 6 spoken? Mark the features of fast speech from exercise 2. Then listen again and check. Practise saying the sentences.**

5D Grammar
Articles and quantifiers
I can use articles and quantifiers.

1 Correct the mistakes with the bold articles in the text.

MOON'S BEST FRIEND

Photographer Ben Moon has made **the** ~~an~~ **emotional short film** about [1]**a best friend** he's ever had: [2]**the dog** called Denali. Denali was just two years old when Ben rescued him from an animal shelter. They spent nearly fifteen years together, travelling around [3]**United States** in [4]**the camper van**, going to the beach and spending time with friends. And when Ben was getting over [5]**the serious illness**, Denali was constantly by his side, sleeping on his hospital bed. [6]**A film** won two awards at a festival in [7]**the Colorado**, and has taken the internet by storm with its moving story of the close friendship Ben and Denali shared for so long.

2 Complete the sentences with *a/an*, *the* or – (no article).

1 _____ film we just watched must be _____ worst I've seen!
2 She works as _____ volunteer, helping _____ elderly.
3 Although I don't generally like _____ cats, I like _____ one next door.
4 Just put _____ shopping on _____ table over there, will you?
5 We met _____ family from _____ Caribbean at the carnival.
6 _____ first camping trip I went on wasn't in _____ Europe.
7 My dad's got _____ new job, but _____ job is in another city.
8 I've got _____ idea: why don't we get _____ takeaway later?

3 Choose the best option (a, b or c) to complete the sentences.

1 The forecast says there will be just ___ rain at the weekend.
  a little   b a little   c a lot of
2 ___ the best music I've heard is on this album.
  a Some of   b Both of   c Several of
3 The children didn't make ___ mess.
  a all of   b a lot of   c much of
4 ___ of my shirts needs washing!
  a Every   b Every one   c All
5 ___ drivers follow the new driving regulations.
  a Some of   b None   c Few
6 I wouldn't recommend ___ of the cafés in town.
  a none   b either   c every one

4 Choose the option that is <u>not</u> possible in each sentence.

1 ___ of these scarves would be a good present for Leo.
  a Either   b Both   c Every
2 ___ her friends was at home when she called.
  a Every one of   b None   c None of
3 There's ___ time before the next lesson begins.
  a little   b few   c a little
4 ___ of us agreed that the exercise was impossible.
  a Every   b Each   c Every one
5 Let's buy ___ these cakes for the picnic.
  a both   b a few of   c several
6 She organised ___ of her books into alphabetical order.
  a every   b all   c every one
7 ___ buddy movies are popular in the USA.
  a Some   b Many   c A lot
8 I know ___ people who are scared of snakes.
  a several   b a lot   c many

5 Complete the sentences with the words below. There are two extra words.

a both few many no none of one

1 It was a pretty boring party as there were so _____ people there.
2 Dan got every _____ of the answers right in yesterday's homework.
3 I only have _____ little cash – could you lend me some?
4 She tried on five pairs of shoes, but _____ of them fitted.
5 'Would you prefer orange or apple juice?' 'I don't mind – I like _____ of them.'
6 The forecast says there'll be _____ sunshine today.

6 Complete the text with one word in each gap.

In [1]_____ recent survey, two thousand British men and women were asked about their friendships. [2]_____ women turned out to be twice as good at making friends for life, with one in three saying that their best friend was someone they had met at school. In contrast, only one in six men were best friends with [3]_____ school friend. Although the men had between fifty and a hundred Facebook friends and fifty friends' numbers in their phones, they only had a [4]_____ close friends – on average, about five. [5]_____ sexes admitted that there was at least one person in their friendship group that they couldn't stand; although not quite as [6]_____ men as women confessed to this, it was still a surprising 13%! [7]_____ survey concluded that all [8]_____ us can expect to have fewer close friends as we get older, with only about three by the time we retire.

5E Word Skills

Phrasal verbs

I can use phrasal verbs.

1 Choose the correct answers to complete the text.

In the teen movie *The Duff*, Bianca is enjoying her senior high school year until her neighbour, Wes, lets slip that she's known as a 'duff' – someone less attractive who makes her friends feel prettier and more popular. Bianca believes that her best friends, Jess and Casey, have ¹__ by making fun of her, so she ²__ their friendship, 'unfriending' them on social media and in person. Bianca's friendship with Wes grows when she ³__ helping her become more popular so that she can get the attention of cool guitar-playing Toby, who she likes. However, bad girl Madison used to ⁴__ Wes and she's jealous because he and Bianca ⁵__ so well. And when Bianca eventually plucks up the courage to ⁶__ on a date, she can't believe he doesn't ⁷__ – but he's only using her to get closer to Jess and Casey! If you want to know how things turn out, you'll have to watch the film for yourself!

1	**a** put her through	**b** let her down	**c** turned her down
2	**a** calls off	**b** puts down	**c** gets over
3	**a** puts him off	**b** puts him through	**c** talks him into
4	**a** go out with	**b** put up with	**c** split up with
5	**a** turn up	**b** get on	**c** look after
6	**a** make Toby up	**b** mess Toby about	**c** ask Toby out
7	**a** turn her down	**b** put her down	**c** put her through

2 Complete the sentences with the correct form of the verbs below.

get over   not get on   not make up   not turn up
put through   talk into

1 I can't believe Ken asked me out on a date and then _____ !

2 Rob had a huge row with Sam last week and they still _____ .

3 Surprisingly, he had no trouble _____ his girlfriend when they split up.

4 I'm so angry. You've _____ me _____ so much recently.

5 I've made my mind up, so don't try _____ me _____ going!

6 It's difficult having friends who _____ with each other.

3 Complete the text with the correct particles.

After my best friend broke ¹_____ with her last boyfriend, Sam, she didn't go ²_____ with anyone for a few months. Sam had been messing her ³_____ for ages and she couldn't put ⁴_____ with it any longer, so in the end, she decided to split ⁵_____ with him. But now she's met someone new. He's picking her ⁶_____ from school later today, so I'll finally get to meet him!

VOCAB BOOST!

When you learn new phrasal verbs, make sure you know if they are separable or inseparable. Use *sth* or *sb* to show the position of the object or write sentences with personal examples to help you remember them.

ask (sb) out (sb): I was pleased when my brother asked out my best friend / asked my best friend out.

bring sth ↔ up 1 to mention a subject or start to talk about it

get over sth/sb to return to your usual state of health, happiness, etc. after an illness, shock, the end of a relationship, etc.

4 Read the *Vocab boost!* box and the dictionary entries. Are the phrasal verbs separable or inseparable? Put them in the correct column in the table. Then add the phrasal verbs below.

call off   let down   look after   run into   take after   turn down

Separable	Inseparable

5 Write sentences to illustrate the meaning of the phrasal verbs in the table in exercise 4.

1 _____ (bring up)
2 _____ (call off)
3 _____ (get over)
4 _____ (let down)
5 _____ (look after)
6 _____ (run into)
7 _____ (take after)
8 _____ (turn down)

Love is in the air

I can understand an article about research into relationships.

Revision: Student's Book page 58

1 Complete the sentences with the words below.

genes   guinea pigs   immune systems   mate
offspring   organs   paper   proof

1 They asked for students to be _____ for their experiment on sleep.
2 Dr Smith is presenting a _____ on her new thermodynamic theory.
3 What _____ have you got to show that your theory is correct?
4 All animals have developed ways of attracting a _____ .
5 The illness can be avoided by modifying the _____ in people's DNA.
6 Our _____ protect us against illness and infection.
7 Birds will protect and feed their _____ until they are able to fly.
8 Hospitals need more donors so that they can replace damaged _____ .

Reading Strategy

When you come across an unfamiliar word in a text, ask yourself if you need to know its meaning to do the task. If you do, first decide what part of speech it is. Then try to work out from the context what it might mean.

2 Read the Reading Strategy. Then read the text and try to guess the meanings of the underlined words from the context. Check your answers in a dictionary.

3 Answer the questions about the article.

Which paragraph mentions ...
1 relationships being formed? ___
2 conversations about views, dreams and beliefs? ___
3 the science of love? ___
4 the aim of the experiment? ___

4 Choose the correct answers (a–d).

1 Thanks to Arthur Aron, we have learned that
 a couples are mistaken about why they fell in love.
 b smell attracts people to each other.
 c love is the result of a chemical reaction.
 d people can fall in love quickly.

2 The aim of Arthur Aron's research was to see
 a if people would fall in love after four minutes.
 b if there was a big difference between fancying someone and loving them.
 c if intimacy could be provoked.
 d how many questions it would take to make people feel close.

3 Aron explained that his questions
 a would make people famous.
 b should be done while people stare at each other.
 c would help people have experiences together.
 d would make people feel that they had a connection.

4 The experiment that tested Aron's theory resulted in
 a some people hoping to stay in contact.
 b a few marriages.
 c all the participants quickly falling in love.
 d only a few of the partners forming a connection.

Love
in 36 questions

A Although couples will rarely believe it, scientific <u>factors</u> have a lot to do with falling in love. Research has shown that scent plays an important role in choosing a mate. Other experiments have demonstrated that love is caused by combinations of chemicals in the brain. Furthermore, New York psychologist Arthur Aron applied the principles of science to demonstrate that the process of falling in love could be speeded up … to just 45 minutes!

B Some scientists claim that we take between ninety seconds and four minutes to decide if we <u>fancy</u> someone. However, the <u>leap</u> from being attracted to someone to falling in love with them is a big one, and Aron wanted to find out if the closeness associated with feelings of being in love could be created artificially.

C Aron produced a paper that included 36 questions designed to encourage <u>intimacy</u> if couples answered them together. The questions came in three sets with each set covering increasingly intimate ground. They covered many personal opinions and experiences; for example, 'Would you like to be famous?', 'What does friendship mean to you?' and 'When did you last cry in front of another person?' After answering the questions together, the couples were directed to stare into each other's eyes for four minutes without saying anything.

D Aron tested his questions on pairs of strangers and then asked them to stare at each other. All of the participants reported feeling close to their partners and many of them <u>swapped</u> contact details after the experiment. So if you're keen on someone and would like to get closer to them, it would seem that Aron's questions could help you to achieve your objective.

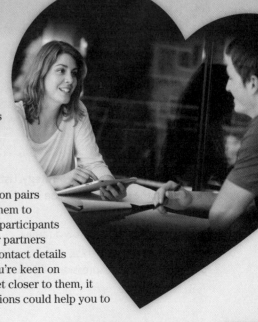

5G Speaking
Photo description and comparison
I can describe and compare photos and give opinions about friendship.

1 **Rewrite the sentences using *must have*, *may (not) have*, or *can't have*.**

1 I'm sure that they were good friends before the argument as they were always together.
_____

2 It's possible that there was a misunderstanding.
_____

3 It's impossible that she said that about her friend.
_____

4 It's certain that she liked her friend's brother.
_____

5 It's possible that he wasn't attracted to her.
_____

6 It's impossible that they went out together.
_____

2 **Look at the photo and write sentences about it. Use *must be / may be / can't be*.**

_____
_____
_____
_____

> **Speaking Strategy**
> When you talk about photos, say what you can guess or deduce as well as about what you can see. Use modal verbs of deduction and phrases such as *It appears to show ...* , *I can't be certain, but ...* , etc.

3 **1.30** **Read the Speaking Strategy. Listen to a student describing the photo in exercise 3 and complete the sentences.**

1 The photo seems to show a family _____ .
2 It looks as if the son is _____ .
3 Judging by their expressions, I'd say that the parents are
_____ .

4 I might be wrong, but I think the mother is asking him to
_____ .
5 I can't be certain, but I don't think she's _____ .
6 The father looks _____ .

4 **Look at photos A and B in exercise 5 below. Complete these sentences with your own ideas.**

Photo A
Judging by the mother's expression, I'd say _____ .
It looks as if the daughter is _____ .
I might be wrong, but I think the father is
_____ .

Photo B
The photo seems to show _____ .
I can't be certain, but I don't think the daughter
_____ .
The son looks _____ .

5 **Look at the task and the photos below. Then read the questions (1–5) and write answers.**

> Compare the photos. Then say whether you think arguments between family members are more or less serious than arguments between friends. Give reasons.

1 What is the common theme of the photos?
_____

2 What can you see in both photos?
_____

3 What is the main difference between the photos?
_____

4 Which are more serious: family arguments or arguments between friends?
_____

5 What are the reasons for your answer to question 4?
_____
_____

6 **Now do the task using your notes from exercise 5.**

5H

An opinion essay

I can write an opinion essay on the topic of friendship.

Preparation

'A friend in need is a friend indeed.' This saying means that a real friend is there for you in times of trouble. Write an essay in which you give your own opinion of this view, taking into consideration the way we make friends these days and situations where you can recognise real friends.

1 Read the task above. How many elements are there to cover?

2 Read the essay. In which paragraphs does the writer cover each element of the task?

> **Writing Strategy**
> Use a variety of grammatical structures and vocabulary instead of simple sentences. This will make your essay more interesting and more effective.

3 Read the Writing Strategy and underline an example of each of the structures below in the essay.

1 contrasting clauses with *but* and *although*
2 an example of another linker
3 an example of preparatory *it*
4 a sentence starting with *Not that ...*
5 an example of *do/did* for emphasis

4 Complete the second sentence so that it means the same as the first.

1 She's a good friend, but she can be a bit moody.
Although _____ .

2 People say that you must be a good friend to have a good friend.
It _____ .

3 Having true friends is important.
It _____ .

4 I tried talking to him, but he didn't understand what I was saying.
I tried talking to him, not that _____ .

5 I try hard, but she won't be friends with me.
I try hard. However, _____ .

5 Rewrite the sentences using *do/did* for emphasis.

1 I liked her.
_____

2 'Why didn't you tell him I was here?' 'I told him!'
_____

3 Although she's twice my age, we have a lot in common.
_____

4 I think he is a good friend.
_____

5 'You don't support me enough.' 'I support you!'
_____

A I find that the saying 'A friend in need is a friend indeed' is a true one and I wholeheartedly agree with it. I do think that a true friend is one who is always there for you, no matter what.

B In the internet age, people are more sociable than ever. It's easy to make lots of friends online because no one makes any demands on you. Not that it isn't good to have a wide circle of people to socialise with. Nevertheless, it is said that most of us can count our number of true friends on the fingers of one hand, and I personally think that it is in times of trouble that you find out who your real friends are.

C I have known my closest friend Mina since primary school and she remains the nicest, gentlest person I know. We rarely have arguments. Not that we agree on everything, but we generally have a caring and supportive relationship. When my mum was very ill in hospital, she was the truest friend of all. She never once complained that I was bad company, like one or two of my other friends, and I could always talk to her about all my fears. This type of situation really shows you who your friends are.

D So, in my view, although you may have lots of friends to have fun with, make sure you have at least one close friend who can support you when you need it most.

Writing Guide

There is a saying 'Age is no barrier to friendship.' Write an essay in which you give your opinion of this view, taking into consideration the generation gap and different life experience.

6 Read the task above. Make some notes for your opinion and personal description.

7 Write your essay.

> **CHECK YOUR WORK**
> **Have you ...**
> ☐ structured your essay with paragraphs?
> ☐ covered and linked the required elements?
> ☐ included a variety of structures?

5 Review Unit 5

Vocabulary

1 Complete the sentences with a verb phrase containing the word in brackets.

1 I _____ Oliver. He hasn't got any friends. (sorry)
2 I _____ my new neighbour. I don't trust him. (wary)
3 Sarah and I seem to be arguing a lot. We don't _____ on several things. (eye)
4 Poppy's my best friend because we have _____ . (common)
5 We have similar ideas. We _____ . (wavelength)
6 Matt adores his elder brother. He really _____ him. (looks)

Mark: ___ / 6

2 Complete the sentences with the words below.

complimented   flattered   lectured   nagged
offended   teased

1 My mum _____ me all weekend about my room. She kept on telling me that I should tidy it.
2 You really _____ me when you said that I'd put on weight. I was quite upset.
3 My host family _____ me on my English. They said it was excellent.
4 Anna's brother _____ her about her new haircut. He said it made her look like a boy.
5 You only _____ me because you wanted something. You don't usually say anything nice.
6 My dad _____ me for an hour about my exam results. He went on and on about 'responsibility'.

Mark: ___ / 6

Word Skills

3 Rewrite the sentences with the phrasal verbs below.

bring up   get over   put down   turn down   turn up

1 We waited, but John didn't arrive.
   _____ .
2 I didn't want to mention it.
   _____ .
3 You're always making me feel stupid.
   _____ .
4 Kate was upset, but she'll recover.
   _____ .
5 They offered me a job, but I rejected it.
   _____ .

Mark: ___ / 5

4 Complete the sentences with one word in each gap.

1 A person's eye colour depends on their g_____ .
2 He wrote an important p_____ that was published in a medical journal.
3 She was lucky that none of her internal o_____ were damaged in the accident.
4 In the animal world, one parent usually stays with the o_____ while the other searches for food.
5 Scientists have formulated a theory, but as yet they have no p_____ .

Mark: ___ / 5

5 Match the sentence halves.

1 He appears   a certain, but I think he's a vet.
2 It looks as   b to be selling something.
3 Judging by   c her face, I'd say she was upset.
4 Nothing   d if she's enjoying herself.
5 I can't be   e springs immediately to mind.

Mark: ___ / 5

Grammar

6 Rewrite the sentences using inversion.

1 I've never been so embarrassed in my life.
   _____ .
2 You shouldn't leave the resort under any circumstances.
   _____ .
3 There won't be another delivery until next week.
   _____ .
4 I ran into an old friend as soon as I left my house.
   _____ .
5 They didn't consider splitting up at any time.
   _____ .
6 We hadn't seen such poverty anywhere before.
   _____ .

Mark: ___ / 6

7 Complete the second sentence so that it means the same as the first. Write five words in each sentence. (Contractions count as two words.)

1 The plate was very hot, but I didn't drop it.
   I managed _____ although it was very hot.
2 Oscar had been offered a job, so he opted out of going to university.
   Oscar chose _____ because he had been offered a job.
3 Living in the country, I don't usually hear very much traffic.
   I'm used to _____ because I live in the country.

4 I thought your sister took her driving test last week.

_____ her driving test last week?

5 I think we should go home now.

_____ now?

Mark: ____ / 5

8 Choose the correct answers (a–c).

An unusual relationship

One of ¹__ strangest friendships in literature occurs in ²__ story by E.B. White called *Charlotte's Web*. ³__ story is set on a farm in ⁴__ USA, where Charlotte – a spider – makes friends with a pig named Wilbur and helps to save his life. Although *Charlotte's Web* was written for ⁵__ children, it is popular with both young and adult readers all over ⁶__ world, and it has sold over 45 million copies in 23 different languages.

1 a a	**b** the	**c** no article
2 a a	**b** the	**c** no article
3 a A	**b** The	**c** no article
4 a a	**b** the	**c** no article
5 a a	**b** the	**c** no article
6 a a	**b** the	**c** no article

Mark: ____ / 6

9 Choose the correct words to complete the text.

Man's best friend

There have been ¹**a lot / many** dogs who have saved their owners, but ²**no / none** of them braver than a golden retriever named Figo. Figo isn't a pet; he's a guide dog for the blind. He has had ³**several / much** different owners, and he's helped ⁴**every / all** of them get around safely outside. On Monday, he was crossing the road with his current owner, Audrey Stone, when a bus didn't stop at the crossing. Figo jumped up at the bus to protect Audrey, who ended up injured, but alive. Figo needed an operation because he had hurt his leg and paw. Luckily, there were ⁵**few / a few** passengers on the bus at the time: only two schoolchildren. ⁶**Either / Neither** of them were injured.

Mark: ____ / 6

Use of English

10 Complete the sentences using the correct form of the words in brackets. Use up to six words, including the words in brackets, and do not change the order of the words.

1 I _____ (not / feel / close) my brother since he got married.

2 My friends _____ (talk / into / play) for their football team, but I got injured in the first match.

3 Sally's mum _____ (tell / off / come) home late last night.

4 The documentary I watched _____ (put / off / eat) meat for life.

5 Not until everyone had taken their seats in the theatre _____ (play / begin).

6 Hardly _____ (reach / platform) when my train arrived.

7 _____ (not / we / meet) somewhere before?

8 Ryan _____ (try / not / think) his ex-girlfriend, but sometimes he finds it impossible.

9 I don't mind watching this film again because _____ (none / my friends / see) it.

10 The comedian was hilarious. We _____ (laugh / every) his jokes.

Mark: ____ / 10

Total: ____ / 60

I can …

Read the statements. Think about your progress and tick one of the boxes.

⭐ = I need more practice.   ⭐⭐⭐ = No problem!

⭐⭐ = I sometimes find this difficult.

	⭐	⭐⭐	⭐⭐⭐
I can talk about relationships and describe behaviour.			
I can use negative structures.			
I can understand a discussion about sibling rivalry.			
I can use articles and quantifiers.			
I can use phrasal verbs.			
I can understand an article that talks about science and experiments.			
I can describe and compare photos and give opinions about friendship.			
I can write an opinion essay on the topic of friendship.			

Health

A Food science

I can talk about nutrition and health.

1 Choose the correct words to complete the text.

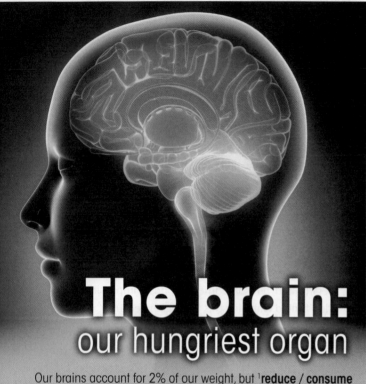

The brain:
our hungriest organ

Our brains account for 2% of our weight, but ¹**reduce / consume** 20% of the energy that our bodies ²**produce / digest** after eating. When we sleep, our brains continue to ³**burn / produce** energy because they are still working. They ⁴**process / burn** all the day's activities and create memories. The brain also repairs itself, but if we don't sleep enough, it ⁵**reduces / burns** the time that our brains have for this work. Having fewer hours of sleep also affects our diets, as it is more difficult for our brains to ⁶**control / process** our weight if we don't sleep enough. If we want to ⁷**consume / boost** our brains' energy levels, we should do exercise. Exercise pumps blood full of oxygen to our brains.

2 Match the verbs below with the definitions. There is one extra verb.

ache   boost   consume   control   digest   process
produce   reduce

1 to use fuel, energy, or time, especially in large amounts
   _____

2 to make something smaller in size, importance, amount, etc. _____

3 to make something _____

4 to improve or increase something _____

5 to change food in your stomach into substances that your body can use _____

6 the feeling you get in your muscles when you've done a lot of exercise _____

7 to order, limit, or rule something _____

3 Complete the words in the sentences.

1 Sausages, sliced ham and bacon can be tasty, but
   p_____ m_____ is not very good for you.

2 You should avoid all types of p_____
   f_____ such as pre-cooked meals.

3 D_____ p_____ like milk and cheese are important for growing children because they strengthen their bones.

4 It's much better to eat brown bread made from
   w_____ g_____ flour rather than processed white bread.

5 Some p_____ farmers keep turkeys and ducks as well as chickens.

4 🎧 2.02 Listen to a nutritionist giving advice about the best food for people who do sport. Tick the things he mentions.

1	calcium	☐	7 minerals	☐
2	calories	☐	8 nutrients	☐
3	carbohydrates	☐	9 preservatives	☐
4	cholesterol	☐	10 protein	☐
5	fat	☐	11 vitamins	☐
6	fibre	☐		

5 🎧 2.02 Listen again and complete the advice with the words you ticked in exercise 4.

✱ You don't have to eat broccoli, which is full of
   ¹_____ , with oil and salt, but it might help to make it tastier!

✱ Sweet potatoes and tomatoes contain a lot of
   ²_____ .

✱ You should try and avoid red meat because although it has ³_____ , it also has a lot of
   ⁴_____ .

✱ You must eat fruit – bananas are a good option because they have a lot of ⁵_____ .

✱ You mustn't eat too many nuts because although they provide you with ⁶_____ , they also contain a lot of ⁷_____ .

✱ If you have to exercise in the evening, milk will help you relax and provide your bones with
   ⁸_____ .

6B Grammar

The passive

I can identify and use different forms of the passive.

1 Choose the correct options (a–c) to complete the text.

Most of us take antibiotics for granted. They ¹___ to treat many illnesses caused by bacteria, and until now, patients ²___ them successfully to prevent infection following minor surgery and routine operations. Now, though, the public ³___ that some bacteria are becoming resistant to antibiotics, and unless action ⁴___ soon, we could be 'back to the dark ages' when people ⁵___ by common illnesses on a regular basis. Experts explain that in a large group of bacteria, there may be some which ⁶___ by antibiotics; when these bacteria survive and reproduce, they increase the number of resistant bacteria to dangerous levels. Now scientists are raising concerns about a possible outbreak of a resistant infection. They predict that two in every five people who are affected by a resistant infection ⁷___ .

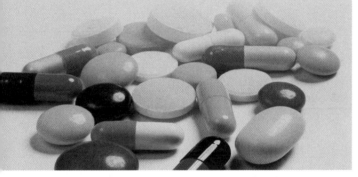

1	a were used	b are used	c had been used
2	a have been given	b are being given	c will be given
3	a were being warned	b are warned	c are being warned
4	a will be taken	b is taken	c has been taken
5	a were killed	b had been killed	c have been killed
6	a are destroyed	b aren't destroyed	c weren't destroyed
7	a have been killed	b are killed	c will be killed

2 Complete the sentences with the correct passive form of the verbs in brackets.

1 Antibiotics _____ (prescribe) by doctors to fight disease for many years.
2 What would our lives be like if X-ray machines _____ (not invent)?
3 Scientists believe that a vaccine to prevent malaria _____ (develop) soon.
4 In the past, many patients _____ (infect) each year in dirty hospitals.
5 Natural plant remedies for illnesses _____ (discover) all the time.
6 Anaesthetics _____ (not use) in operations until the 19th century.

3 Rewrite each sentence in two ways, using the underlined words as the subjects and leaving out the agent.

1 The teacher gave <u>each student</u> <u>a book</u>.
   Each student was given a book.
   A book was given to each student.
2 They have offered <u>both of us</u> <u>a place at university</u>.
   _____
3 Mum cooked <u>me</u> <u>a special dinner</u> last night.
   _____
4 She's lending <u>the money</u> to <u>Anna</u>.
   _____
5 My best friend has just sent <u>me</u> <u>a text message</u>.
   _____
6 Do you think they'll give <u>him</u> <u>the job</u>?
   _____

4 Complete the text with the correct passive form of the verbs below.

bite   cause   give   improve   know   raise

Louis Pasteur ¹_____ as the scientist who proved 'germ theory' after he discovered that many illnesses ²_____ by tiny organisms. He ³_____ in France, and it was there that farmers asked the scientist to investigate why their wine turned sour; Pasteur discovered that heating the wine destroyed the harmful bacteria which made the wine go off. He later focused on human medicine. A woman took her son to Pasteur because the boy ⁴_____ by a dog suffering from rabies; Pasteur cured him in the first-known attempt at vaccination, a process in which a person ⁵_____ a small amount of a dead or weak germ, so that they produce antibodies that fight the disease. Medicine ⁶_____ hugely thanks to Pasteur, as vaccination prevents millions of deaths every year.

5 Complete the second sentence using the correct passive tense so that it means the same as the first.

1 I definitely didn't break the laptop.
   The laptop _____ .
2 Has someone invited Jan to the cinema?
   Has _____ to the cinema?
3 They hadn't told us about the school trip.
   We _____ the school trip.
4 Our teacher will explain the answers next week.
   The answers _____ our teacher next week.
5 They were showing students around the museum.
   Students _____ around the museum.
6 The government is advising people not to travel there.
   People _____ travel there.

Keeping fit

I can listen to and understand people talking about exercise.

Revision: Student's Book page 67

1 **Complete the sentences with the correct form of the words below.**

adrenalin   burn   burst   convert   energy
high-intensity   pump

1 When you are exercising, the body _____ fat and sugar into _____ so that you can keep going.
2 Running fast releases _____ , which helps you to _____ fat.
3 The most effective way to get fit is by doing short _____ of _____ exercise.
4 If you exercise hard, you can feel your heart _____ .

2 **Complete the sentences with the correct form of the verbs below.**

attend   be   beat   do   go   keep   lift   pedal   play   push

1 I play to win – I _____ quite competitive and I'm never happier than when I've _____ an opponent.
2 I never _____ running alone after dark.
3 I enjoy _____ fit. It makes me feel healthy.
4 I train hard and always _____ myself to the limit.
5 My dad regularly _____ weights in the gym, but he hurt his back last week.
6 My mum _____ a lot of fitness classes at the local gym, but she likes _____ aerobics most of all.
7 My brother _____ on an exercise bike in his bedroom. He says it's safer than going outside!
8 He doesn't enjoy _____ football. He prefers swimming and running.

Listening Strategy
Remember that the information in the task may be expressed in a different way in the text.

3 🎧 **2.03 Read the Listening Strategy. Then read the sentences and listen to five speakers. What words did the speakers actually use to express these things?**

1 Speaker 1 dislikes exercising.

_____

_____

2 Speaker 2 wonders why his chosen sport is unpopular with his peers.

_____

_____

3 Speaker 3 talks about the body's preferred form of exercise.

_____

_____

4 Speaker 4 describes her family's favourite pastime.

_____

_____

5 Speaker 5 explains how what we eat is converted into fuel for the body.

_____

_____

4 🎧 **2.04 Listen to four texts where people talk about their preferred form of exercising. Choose the correct answers (a–c).**

Text 1

1 These speakers explain
  a how their favourite activity doesn't involve teamwork.
  b that they don't like the gym or sports.
  c what it takes to succeed in their favourite activity.

Text 2

2 This speaker's intention is to
  a detail his sport's training regime.
  b explain why the sport's rules are important.
  c warn that his sport is very dangerous.

Text 3

3 This speaker is explaining
  a the effects of exercise on the various muscle groups.
  b how exercise also affects the mind.
  c that exercise must be regular to be beneficial.

Text 4

4 This speaker talks about
  a how much he enjoys training with his father.
  b why his father is paying for his training.
  c how difficult the training is for a triathlon.

The passive: advanced structures

I can use advanced passive structures.

1 Complete the passive sentences with the correct form of the modal verbs and verbs in brackets.

1 It isn't true that sleepwalkers _____ (can't / wake) safely.

2 It seems that more research into the new drug _____ (ought to / do) before it was made available.

3 Surely the results of the tests _____ (must / check) before they were published?

4 Our sleep _____ (can / disturb) by artificial lighting.

5 Perhaps not all health myths _____ (should / dismiss) completely.

6 We _____ (might / lie) to for decades by the drinks industry about how much water we need.

7 Some health advice _____ (may / misunderstand) in the past.

8 Do you think most smokers _____ (could / encourage) to quit by using e-cigarettes?

2 Complete the text with the correct passive infinitive or *-ing* form of the verb in brackets.

Imagine ¹_____ (wake up) by a member of your family to discover that you have not only got out of bed and turned on your computer while asleep, but have emailed your friends without knowing it. Apparently, cases of 'zzz-mailing' are starting ²_____ (report) more frequently, and experts say they expect ³_____ (tell) about even more of these strange events. Robert Wood, who suffers from bizarre night-time wanderings, desperately hopes ⁴_____ (cure) after his wife, who didn't expect ⁵_____ (meet) by such a worrying sight, found the Scottish chef cooking chips in their kitchen while fast asleep! However, another sufferer, nurse Lee Hadwin, definitely doesn't want ⁶_____ (prevent) from sleepwalking and admits ⁷_____ (amaze) by his unconscious talents! He certainly deserves ⁸_____ (know) as a gifted artist after producing amazing drawings on tablecloths, clothes and walls – although it seems he has no such ability while he's awake.

Lee Hadwin with one of his night time drawings

3 Rewrite the sentences in two ways using passive structures. Begin with the words given.

1 We know that too much sugar is bad for us.
It is _____
Too much sugar_____

2 They estimate that a third of babies born in the UK in 2013 have a life expectancy of 100.
It is _____
A third _____

3 They say that vitamin C is good for colds.
It is _____
Vitamin C _____

4 People once thought that carrots were good for your eyesight.
It was once _____
Carrots were once _____

5 People believe that the ancient Egyptians were great doctors.
It is _____
The ancient Egyptians _____

6 They say that the actor put on ten kilos for this film.
It is _____
The actor _____

4 Complete the text with one word in each gap.

Do you hate ¹_____ told that you should be drinking more water? ²_____ is often reported that we ought to drink at least two litres a day, but there are many people who believe this advice must have ³_____ spread by companies wanting us to buy their bottled water. Humans are known to ⁴_____ evolved in conditions of extreme heat and dryness and it ⁵_____ now thought that too much water is worse for us than too little. According to one scientist, it's like saying we should all ⁶_____ encouraged to breathe more oxygen, because if a little is good for us, more must be even better!

Word Skills
Compound adjectives
I can use compound adjectives.

1 Match the sentence halves.

1 It was such a far- ☐
2 We're taking a much- ☐
3 My uncle used to be a highly ☐
4 She's so single- ☐
5 Your actions could have far- ☐
6 The film is a light- ☐
7 Being absent- ☐
8 She made a half- ☐

a hearted look at the world of fashion.
b needed break in the country next weekend.
c reaching consequences for all of us.
d minded, I often forget things.
e fetched story that no one believed him.
f hearted effort, but wasn't really trying.
g trained athlete many years ago.
h minded that you won't change her decision.

2 Complete the sentences with the words below.

breath   high   mouth   old   second   thought   time

1 We had a _____taking view from the top of the mountain.
2 This phone is considered very _____-fashioned nowadays.
3 I'd never eaten such _____-watering dishes before I visited Thailand.
4 Last night's TV fashion documentary was informative and _____-provoking.
5 If you don't like _____-spirited dogs, I don't recommend this breed.
6 Despite all the _____-saving devices I own, I always seem to be busy!
7 Most people own _____-hand cars as new ones are so expensive.

3 Complete the sentences with a compound adjective formed from the word in brackets.

1 It may be an interesting article, but it's not very _____ (write).
2 If Zoe's as _____ (look) as her sister, she must be really beautiful!
3 Isn't that man sitting opposite a _____ (know) singer?
4 This job's only suitable for people from _____ (speak) countries such as the UK or Australia.
5 Japan is a very _____ (populated) country.
6 Travelling into space must be a _____ (blow) experience!
7 I'm always _____ (eye) until I've had some coffee.

It may be surprising, but scientists still have no ¹___ explanation for why we dream. There are plenty of ²___ facts about dreams, but little agreement about their purpose. Many ³___ scientists think that dreams allow a ⁴___ opportunity for the brain to clear its 'hard disk' while we sleep. Others are more interested in the meaning of dreams, and although it may seem ⁵___, some people are said to have predicted the future while dreaming. There is much that is ⁶___ about dreams, so when you next wake up ⁷___ from a good night's sleep, why not try writing down your dreams as soon as you wake up? Because apparently, 95% of what you dream is forgotten before you get out of bed!

4 Choose the correct options (a–c) to complete the text above.

1 a single-minded   b straightforward   c far-reaching
2 a well-known   b good-looking   c well-written
3 a mind-blowing   b highly respected   c badly paid
4 a time-saving   b second-hand   c much-needed
5 a far-fetched   b half-hearted   c high-spirited
6 a upcoming   b thought-provoking   c old-fashioned
7 a light-hearted   b bleary-eyed   c absent-minded

VOCAB BOOST!
Not all compound adjectives, especially those formed from adverb + past participle, appear in a dictionary because they are formed from other words. You should be able to work out the meaning of most of them from the words which form them. For example, a *highly paid* person is someone who is paid a lot of money.

5 Read the *Vocab boost!* box. Then complete the second part of each sentence with an explanation. Try not to repeat the words from the compound adjective.

1 A short-sighted person is someone _____ _____ .
2 A cold-blooded animal is an animal _____ _____ .
3 A last-minute decision is a decision _____ _____ .
4 A world-famous tourist attraction is one _____ _____ .
5 A well-behaved child is a child _____ _____ .
6 A deeply rooted tradition is a tradition _____ _____ .
7 An open-minded person is someone _____ _____ .

Future food

I can understand a text about insects as food.

Revision: Student's Book page 70

1 Complete the text with the words below.

amounts diet dishes flavours leftovers menu
portion slice

I'm trying to improve my ¹_____ , but it isn't easy if you love all types of food like I do. However, I've decided that instead of not eating my favourite meals, I'll just eat smaller ²_____ of them. That means that I'll eat a ³_____ of pizza and not a whole one, and I'll just have one ⁴_____ of takeaway Chinese food instead of two. At least that means there won't be any ⁵_____ filling up the fridge! And when I eat out at a restaurant, I'll choose the meals on the ⁶_____ that include salads and healthy food. The problem is that I like food with strong ⁷_____ and tastes, so I'm going to find ⁸_____ full of lettuce a bit tasteless!

2 Read the text and answer the questions.

1 What reasons are used to support an insect-based diet?
2 How are supporters of insects as food trying to persuade Americans to eat them?

Reading Strategy

When you do a gapped sentence task, look for clues before and after each gap. For example, if a sentence starts with *And* or *Furthermore*, it probably introduces additional information.

Other words can be used for

• contrast: *But, However*
• consequences or conclusions: *So, Therefore*

3 Read the Reading Strategy. Then read the text again. Match sentences A–E with gaps 1–4. There is one extra sentence.

A Today, 50% of the same universities promote insects as food.
B The popularity of Mexican food in the USA is also helping, as companies such as Don Bugito offer traditional Mexican insect dishes.
C Moreover, the amount of land needed to produce enough insects to feed the whole country is much smaller than the land needed to produce meat.
D But will it be enough?
E However, in parts of Asia, Africa and Central America, where there are plenty of big, juicy insects all year round, they are considered a delicious staple.

THE INSECTS ARE COMING!

With an abundance of cheap food and a weakness for junk food, the dietary habits of many Americans (and people in other Western countries) have led to an obesity epidemic. As a result, a growing number of food experts are saying it's time to replace traditional dishes with more nutritious and also more economical and ecological dishes: dishes that contain insects.

If you put a plate of bugs (as insects are often called in the USA) in front of an American, they, like most Westerners, would probably refuse to eat them. Insects are seen as pests that destroy food crops rather than delicacies to be eaten. ¹___ The challenge for the promoters of insect-based meals is to make Americans see them in the same way.

During the 20th century, if you had visited a research department at an American food and agricultural university, you would have heard about how they were trying to reduce insect numbers due to the negative impact they have on crops and seeds. ²___ Furthermore, insect fairs such as the BugFest at the North Carolina Museum or The Great Insect Fair at Penn State University explain that grasshoppers, moths and their cousins are an excellent source of nutrients like protein, minerals and vitamins. The fairs also offer the more adventurous visitors 'bug banquets', which serve mouth-watering insect dishes.

Apart from the scientific community, a growing number of market stalls and restaurants are providing insect meals too. ³___ What is more, fans of insect-based cooking like Daniella Martin are spreading the word that bugs are good for you. Martin's blog *Girl Meets Bug*, her internet cooking videos and her newspaper columns are all contributing to changing Americans' perceptions of insects. ⁴___ While entomophagists (people who eat insects) agree they face an uphill struggle, with 70 million obese citizens and millions more who want to be environmentally friendly, it seems that this could be the right time for insects to invade America's kitchens.

Role-play

I can role-play a conversation at the doctor's.

Revision: Student's Book page 72

1 Match the illnesses and injuries with the treatments.

1	virus	a	antibiotics
2	chest infection	b	throat sweets / painkillers
3	heartburn	c	X-ray
4	sore throat	d	antacids
5	sprain	e	antiseptic cream
6	fracture	f	bandage / anti-inflammatories
7	cut	g	antihistamine
8	bee sting	h	rest and lots of liquids

Speaking Strategy

Do not get nervous if you're unsure whether you've understood the question or what the other person has said. Simply ask the person for clarification.

2 Read the Speaking Strategy and complete the sentences with the phrases below.

could repeat that?   like … ?   mean by … ?   quite catch that.   same as … ?   saying that again?

1 Sorry, do you think you _____
2 I'm afraid I didn't _____
3 Would you mind _____
4 What do you _____
5 Is that something _____
6 Is that the _____

3 🎧 2.05 Listen to a student doing the task below. Which two sentences from exercise 2 did the student use?

While on holiday in the UK, you go and see the doctor because you have hurt your ankle. Have a conversation with him/her and discuss the following points:
- the injury
- how you did it
- X-ray and treatment
- a follow-up visit

4 🎧 2.05 Listen again. Make notes on the following topics.

The injury
_____
_____

How the person did it
_____
_____

Treatment
_____
_____

Follow-up visit
_____
_____

What the student needed clarification on
_____
_____

While on holiday in the UK, you suffer from a bad, itchy rash and go and see the doctor. Have a conversation with him/her and discuss the following points:
- when it appeared
- the possible causes
- treatment
- a follow-up visit

5 Read the task. Prepare notes in answer to what the doctor will say. Ask for clarification on one of the questions. Try to give extra detail in your answers.

1 What seems to be the matter?
_____
_____

2 When did the rash appear?
_____
_____

3 What do you think might have caused it?
_____
_____

4 Do you have any allergies?
_____
_____

5 Well, I'm not sure. I'm going to write you a prescription for some antihistamine tablets and cream.
_____

6 If it's still bothering you, or if you feel poorly, come back in a few days.
_____

6 Now do the task using your notes from exercise 5.

6H

An article

I can write an article for a school website.

Preparation

You've read a report about a decline in PE lessons for young people during school hours, especially during exam time. Write an article for your school website about the benefits of teenagers taking regular exercise at this time, and how students could incorporate more of it into their lives.

1 Read the task above. Identify the elements that need to be included in the article. How many paragraphs do you think it should have? Read the article and check.

2 Find four comment adverbs in the article. Write down four more comment adverbs.

_____ _____ _____ _____

_____ _____ _____ _____

> ### Writing Strategy
> Organise your ideas or opinions into a coherent argument by using linking words or phrases, for example: *therefore, although, furthermore, as a result.*

3 Read the Writing Strategy. Find and underline six different conjunctions in the article (excluding *and*, *as* and *when*).

4 Link the sentences using the words below.

although   moreover   since   so   therefore   whereas

1 She runs regularly. She's very fit.

_____

2 He doesn't like exercising much. He still does it.

_____

3 Exercise increases your muscle strength. It improves your brain power.

_____

4 He has a lot of fizzy drinks. His teeth aren't good.

_____

5 Sweets are unhealthy. Fruit is good for you.

_____

6 We've been exercising. We've lost weight.

_____

Writing Guide

You've read an article about the increase in childhood obesity through poor diet and lack of exercise. Write an article for your school website about the risks associated with obesity and propose ways of persuading young people to make good lifestyle choices.

5 Read the task above and make notes on your ideas for each paragraph. Choose a title. Plan your article.

Paragraph 1 _____

Paragraph 2 _____

Paragraph 3 _____

Paragraph 4 _____

KEEP ON MOVING!

It is said that due to academic pressures, many older students in Britain do not have the time in their school schedules for more than two hours of PE a week. Surely this is not enough for young people to maintain healthy lifestyles?

Obviously, students see studying for exams as their overriding priority, as it is vital for good grades and future careers. However, it is simply not healthy for students to spend all their time at their desks. Interestingly, research has shown that regular exercise boosts concentration, reduces stress and aids restful sleep. Consequently, it would appear that exercise is highly important when it comes to successful studying. Therefore, if the school is unable to include enough exercise in students' school timetables, the students should take responsibility for it themselves.

Naturally, I think there are other ways for students to ensure they get enough exercise, for example by walking or cycling to school. Moreover, after-school clubs offer various types of exercise. So too do local leisure centres. It is merely a question of having the will power to organise exercise and stick to it. Once students feel the benefit of regular exercise, it is easier for them to maintain it.

Personally, I think it is extremely important that young people realise that continuing exercise during periods of intense study can help them achieve higher grades. So, let's make a move today!

6 Write your article.

> ### CHECK YOUR WORK
> **Have you ...**
> ☐ organised your ideas into paragraphs?
> ☐ used conjunctions to link your ideas in each paragraph?
> ☐ included one or two comment adverbs?

Vocabulary

1 Complete the sentences with the words below.

calories   carbohydrates   dairy products
minerals   preservatives   pulses

1 People burn _____ when they do exercise.
2 Nuts, eggs and _____ are good sources of protein.
3 _____ can be found in bread, rice, pasta and potatoes.
4 _____ contain calcium, which makes teeth and bones stronger.
5 Processed food contains _____ so that it doesn't go off.
6 Salt is one of the most common _____ found in food, but there are many others.

Mark: ____ / 6

2 Match the verbs in A with the words in B to make collocations. Then complete the sentences.

A be   beat   convert   keep   lift   pedal   play   push

B an opponent   a team sport   competitive   fit
   food into energy   on a bike   weights   yourself to the limit

1 If you want to _____ that isn't football, why not try rugby?
2 My mum tries to _____ by going running every morning.
3 The eight B vitamins help the body _____ so that we are always ready for action.
4 When exercising, I think you should train as intensively as you can. It's only when you _____ that you get results.
5 You should use the right technique to _____ so as not to injure yourself.
6 I'm always over the moon when I _____ at tennis, because I usually lose.
7 Playing sports at school encourages children to _____ which helps them to have higher expectations and achieve better results.
8 In my opinion, you should cycle outdoors as much as possible. It's just not the same when you _____ in the gym.

Mark: ____ / 8

Word Skills

3 Complete the sentences with compound adjectives formed from the words in brackets.

1 The film was more than a little _____ . It was completely unbelievable! (fetch)
2 I've just read a rather _____ article. I'll send it to you, if you like. (provoke)
3 Max is still a bit _____ because he's only just got up. (eye)
4 The size of the new stadium is _____ . It's absolutely huge! (blow)
5 Once again, Usain Bolt has given another _____ performance in the 100 metres. (break)
6 There are so many _____ desserts on the menu. I don't know which one to choose! (water)

Mark: ____ / 6

4 Match the words below with the definitions (1–6).

diet   dish   flavour   leftovers   portion   slice

1 Food that remains at the end of a meal. _____
2 How food or drink tastes. _____
3 A thin piece of food that is cut off a larger portion.
   _____
4 Food served as part of a meal. _____
5 The food that you eat and drink regularly. _____
6 An amount of food that is given to one person.
   _____

Mark: ____ / 6

5 Choose the correct answers (a–c).

1 The doctor says I've got a throat infection, so he's prescribing ___ .
   a antibiotics   b antihistamines
   c antiseptic creams
2 Why don't you take ___ if you've got heartburn?
   a a painkiller   b an antacid
   c an anti-inflammatory
3 The best thing for itchy insect stings is ___ .
   a antibiotics   b painkillers   c antihistamines
4 My sprained ankle is rather swollen, so I'm taking ___ .
   a antacids   b anti-inflammatories   c antibiotics
5 Alex is taking ___ to stop his fractured leg from hurting so much.
   a painkillers   b antihistamines   c antacids

Mark: ____ / 5

6 Complete the sentences asking for clarification.

1 Would you _____ saying that again?
2 Is that something _____ lasagne?
3 What do you _____ by 'far-reaching'?
4 I'm afraid I didn't quite _____ that.
5 Is that the same _____ wholegrain?
6 Sorry, do you think you could _____ that, please?

Mark: ___ / 6

Grammar

7 Rewrite the sentences in the passive. Do not include the agent.

1 Someone has stolen my mountain bike.

_____

2 They are building a new sports centre.

_____

3 They'll postpone the race if it rains.

_____

4 They had cancelled our flight.

_____

5 They're going to close the swimming pool.

_____

6 They cut the grass every week.

_____

Mark: ___ / 6

8 Rewrite the sentences in two different ways using passive structures. Begin with the words given.

1 People think the new coach is a woman.
It _____
_____ .
The new coach _____
_____ .

2 We believe the manager resigned last night.
It _____
_____ .
The manager _____
_____ .

3 They say the rules are straightforward.
It _____
_____ .
The rules _____
_____ .

4 The press reports that some athletes have made a complaint.
It _____
_____ .
Some athletes _____
_____ .

Mark: ___ / 8

Use of English

9 Complete the text with the correct form of the words in brackets.

Should I exercise when I'm sick?

It's a question that occurs to many athletes faced with a major competition. You've worked your training programme up to the [1]_____ (intense) required and then you suddenly wake up [2]_____ (feel) ill. If it's a simple cold, it's fine to train for a short period at a much slower pace. However, if you're more [3]_____ (congest) than that, even the most [4]_____ (mind) athlete should not contemplate doing exercise. Training while sick can have [5]_____ (reach) consequences and there's a logical explanation for this. During an [6]_____ (infect), the body modifies its behaviour. Your body makes substances to fight the attack. Muscle protein, instead of fat, is [7]_____ (break) down for energy. At this point, there's a greater risk of [8]_____ (injure) if you try to continue your training regime. It may take a few weeks to recover your [9]_____ (fit), but this is a small price to pay compared to suffering a serious injury.

Mark: ___ / 9

Total: ___ / 60

I can ...

Read the statements. Think about your progress and tick one of the boxes.

★ = I need more practice.   ★★★ = No problem!
★★ = I sometimes find this difficult.

	★	★★	★★★
I can talk about nutrition and health.			
I can identify and use different forms of the passive.			
I can listen to and understand people talking about exercise.			
I can use advanced passive structures.			
I can use compound adjectives.			
I can react to an article about food addictions.			
I can role-play a conversation at the doctor's.			
I can write an article for a school website.			

Exam Skills Trainer

Reading

1 Read the Strategy. Then read the question and the text below. How many statements does the paragraph match? Which statements are they?

The activity the author mentions

1 requires more effort than you think.

2 makes you ache all over.

3 is much easier than people think.

4 helps avoid getting hurt while exercising.

As the name suggests, boxing yoga is a kind of yoga based on the movements used in boxing. It's supposed to strengthen, condition and stretch the whole body, as well as prevent sporting injuries. Some gyms have free boxing yoga classes, while others charge per session, but there's also a video you can pay to download. It's a pretty strenuous form of exercise, considering it's yoga, but it makes you feel relaxed and energetic afterwards.

2 Read the text and questions 1–6 below. Match the correct question with each part of the text (A–C). You can match each part with more than one question.

In which paragraph does the author mention an activity which ...

1 has become extremely popular recently? ___

2 requires you to do two things at once? ___

3 has made an existing form of exercise more extreme? ___

4 gives the wrong impression to the observer? ___

5 tires you out after a very short time? ___

6 can be particularly painful? ___

The latest fitness trends

A Reformer Pilates is a much more intense form of Pilates. It involves doing the same sort of pushing and stretching exercises, but on equipment resembling a rowing machine. It isn't the kind of thing you'd have at home, so you have to go to a special Pilates centre to try it. If you do, bear in mind that you won't be able to walk up or down stairs for a few days afterwards. At first, it looks quite easy, but towards the end of the session, your thighs will be crying out for mercy.

B Jumping up and down on a trampoline is a lot of fun, but it can make a great workout too. You'd be surprised by how exhausted you are after only a few minutes bouncing. Not only is it better for the heart than running, but it also increases co-ordination and helps reduce stress levels. Trampolining is taking off in a big way, and some new centres have as many as 150 trampolines. You can either have a go at 'freejumping' – without an instructor – or pay someone to teach you how to do it properly.

C If you're usually quite active, but you're feeling down in the dumps, then you might like to try Dynamic Running Therapy – going out for a run with a therapist. The sessions are quite pricey as the therapists are professionals and they charge a bit more than the going rate. It's easier to do both activities when you're running and talking at the same time: you run further because you don't notice your sore feet, and you talk more freely than you would in the therapist's office.

Listening

3 Read the Strategy. Then read the questions in exercise 4. Which one does not ask you to find specific information? Is this question related to the context or the main idea?

4 🎧 2.06 You will hear an interview with Dr Marilyn Shepherd about food safety. Answer questions 1–5. Choose the correct answer, A, B, C, or D.

1 In order to minimise the risk from raw chicken, Dr Shepherd recommends
   A maintaining it at a constant temperature until using it.
   B handling it with clean hands and utensils.
   C keeping it wrapped and placing it in the fridge.
   D checking that it contains no bacteria before cooking it.

2 Dr Shepherd suggests that the best way to find out if chicken is cooked properly is
   A to check that the juices are pink when you cut it.
   B to test the part where the meat is the deepest.
   C to cut a piece from one end and taste it.
   D to use a food thermometer to ensure it has reached 70°C.

3 Dr Shepherd explains that beef is different from other kinds of meat because
   A bacteria tend to stay on the surface.
   B it mustn't be cooked right through to the middle.
   C it doesn't contain any harmful bacteria.
   D the guidelines on handling it are stricter.

4 Microwaves are effective at killing bacteria
   A in food which hasn't been put in the fridge.
   B in all kinds of food except rice.
   C in food that was originally heated to 74°C.
   D in food that has been heated up evenly.

5 What might be the title of Dr Shepherd's talk?
   A How to tell if food has gone off
   B How to treat food poisoning
   C How to take care of what you eat
   D How to organise your fridge

Use of English

5 Read the Strategy. Complete the sentences with the correct form of the verb *be*. Why is this form used in each case?

1 Rice _____ eaten all over the word, especially in Asia.
2 They _____ still having dinner when we popped round to see them.
3 I've _____ thinking about becoming a vegetarian.
4 You'll _____ hungry if you don't have any breakfast.
5 Stop _____ so stubborn and let me help you.

6 Read the text and complete the gaps. Use one word only in each gap.

The truth about superfoods

The term 'superfood' refers to a food that is an especially rich source of a particular nutrient, such as a vitamin or a mineral. Thanks to ambiguous reports in the media, the general public has [1]_____ led to believe that these foods contain large amounts of all the nutrients. While most fruit and vegetables are high in nutrients, the truth is that there are [2]_____ foods that contain all of the vitamins and minerals the body requires daily. In fact, the idea that people [3]_____ only be eating certain superfoods can lead to other important food groups [4]_____ ignored. Neither is a diet based on superfoods necessarily a balanced diet. Avocados, for example, contain a number of important nutrients, but they are extremely high in calories. [5]_____ no circumstances should they be eaten too often. On the other [6]_____ , pomegranates provide the same kind of nutrients, but they have a much lower profile [7]_____ avocados. [8]_____ the whole, it is better not to trust claims that a food is a superfood, and to do your own research into the food instead.

Speaking

7 Read the Strategy. Then rewrite the sentences.

1 It's possible the man is the boy's grandfather.
The man may _____ .
2 I'm pretty sure they've just been shopping.
They must _____ .
3 I think they're having a good time.
They appear to _____ .

8 Look at the two photos below that show different people preparing food. Compare the photos using the points below.

- who is preparing the food
- what food is being prepared
- where it is being prepared
- who is probably going to eat it

Writing

9 Read the strategy. Then choose the best alternatives to complete the text below.

Hungry brains

[1]**It's well established that / Did you know that** the brain is an energy-hungry organ? Despite being relatively small, it uses more than 20% of our daily energy intake. [2]**In my opinion, / That's why** it needs calories to function well. [3]**Can we still feed our brains / Will it be good or bad for us** if schools stop selling high-energy foods in vending machines?

10 Read the task below and write your article.

You see this notice in an international English-language magazine for teenagers.

ARTICLES WANTED!

We're looking for articles about cooking disasters.

Have you or a member of your family ever had a cooking disaster? Tell us about it – describe the dish, and explain what went wrong. The best articles will be published in our next issue.

7 Tall stories

Vocabulary

A Truth and lies
I can talk about telling the truth and lies.

1 Complete the text with the correct form of the verbs below.

disguise   exaggerate   lie   manipulate   pass   photoshop

You can't say that adverts ¹_____ about products to consumers, but I think it's true to say they ²_____ what products can do. Advertisers try to ³_____ our emotions with images of attractive people and places. Furthermore, they have been known to ⁴_____ images so that products look better than they really are. Often, food and drinks manufacturers ⁵_____ off products which have too much sugar as 'energy food' and ⁶_____ the fact that some products contain ingredients that are not good for us.

▌Taste the **goodness!**

2 Complete the sentences with the correct form of the verbs.

cheat   fabricate   fib   fool   mislead   swear

1 Sam was told to leave the exam because he was using his mobile phone and _____ .
2 The children were _____ when they said that the dog ate the cake.
3 You have to _____ to tell the truth in a court of law.
4 That tattoo isn't real! She's just trying to _____ us.
5 The thief claims that the police _____ the evidence against him.
6 Jack _____ his parents about what he had really been doing on Friday evening.

3 🎧 2.07 Listen to the dialogues and choose the correct answers (a–c).

Dialogue 1

1 What is Jessica doing at the beginning of the dialogue?
  a Making an excuse **b** Telling the truth   **c** Cheating
2 What does Tom want Jessica to do?
  a Deceive somebody
  b Lie about something to somebody
  c Own up to something
3 What does Jessica find difficult to do?
  a Tell a lie   **b** Tell the truth   **c** Fool Tom

Dialogue 2

4 What is Grace doing?
  a Photoshopping a picture
  b Disguising her friend
  c Telling the truth
5 What does Grace say she hasn't done?
  a Improved the story
  b Made the story more amusing
  c Fabricated a story
6 What does Leo think a newspaper should do?
  a Portray things as more interesting than they are
  b Tell the truth
  c Reveal secrets

4 Complete the sentences with the correct verbs.

1 A lot of people won't tell you anything face to face, but then r_____ all their secrets on the internet.
2 Nicola l_____ to me about the date of her party!
3 He always m_____ excuses for his mistakes and never accepts responsibility for anything!
4 Alex o_____ up to breaking the window and promised to pay for a new one.
5 The machine d_____ his voice so you didn't know who was speaking.

5 Choose the correct words to complete the sentences.

1 The newspapers gave a very **biased** / **manipulative** report and criticised the government.
2 It's so **honest** / **hypocritical** to tell people to help when you don't do anything yourself!
3 Andy is really **manipulative** / **direct** and tries to control everything so that it always favours him.
4 I like Sara's **direct** / **ethical** manner, even if she sometimes criticises what I have done.
5 There are new medical treatments such as gene therapy which raise **ethical** / **dishonest** issues.
6 I wanted to give Frank an **open** / **honest** answer, but I couldn't tell him his suit looked awful, could I?

6 Match the adjectives below with the descriptions.

devious   fake   hypocritical   straight   trustworthy   truthful

1 Someone who is honest and says what they think. _____
2 Someone who tricks others in order to get what they want. _____
3 Something which is not genuine. _____
4 Someone who can be relied upon to do the right thing and to be honest. _____
5 Someone who says only what is true. _____
6 Someone who says one thing, but does another. _____

Grammar

Reported speech

I can report what people have said and asked.

1 Change the direct speech into reported speech.

1 'You must take these tablets twice a day.'
The doctor says I _____ .

2 'I'm going to the gym tomorrow.'
Ben told me _____ .

3 'You don't have to wait for me.'
Liz said that I _____ .

4 'I took my final exam yesterday.'
Jack told me _____ .

5 'I haven't told you the complete truth.'
Pablo said _____ .

6 'I'll meet you later today.'
Jim tells me _____ .

7 'I prefer this café to the one opposite.'
Julia says _____ .

8 'I'll always remember meeting you.'
Ann told me _____ .

2 Complete the sentences with the correct form of the words in brackets. Do not change the order of the words. Use a maximum of five words including the words in brackets.

1 Will asked us _____ (time / game / start) the next day.

2 The assistant asked him if _____ (he / like / try) on a smaller jacket.

3 My teacher asked me _____ (I / finish) the exercise and I said I hadn't.

4 I asked Maria _____ (which / film / seen) the night before.

5 The dentist asked _____ (me / why) never used an electric toothbrush before.

6 She asked him if _____ (he / going) the park and he said he wasn't.

7 I asked the policeman whether _____ (he / help / us) and he said he could.

3 Change the direct speech into reported speech. Begin with *My mum asked me.*

1 'Why are you home so late?'
_____

2 'Did you leave school on time today?'
_____

3 'You've got lots of homework to do, haven't you?'
_____

4 'When are you going to tidy your room?'
_____

5 'Have you seen your brother this afternoon?'
_____

6 'Will you help me with the shopping tomorrow?'
_____

7 'Would you like me to give you some money for a pizza?'

4 Report the dialogue using *say* or *ask* in the past simple.

Dan Are you going to the concert tomorrow evening?

Zoe No, I'm not. I haven't got any money.

Dan I'll lend you some. How much do you need?

Zoe That's really kind of you, but I have to finish my homework too.

Dan Would you like me to help you finish it?

Zoe Do you speak German?

Dan No, I don't. Your cousin does, doesn't she?

Zoe Yes, she does. Perhaps I should ask her.

_____
_____
_____
_____
_____
_____
_____
_____
_____

5 Write a second sentence that has a similar meaning to the first. Use the words in brackets.

1 'Do you know the answer to these questions?' Sally asked me. (if)
_____

2 'I mustn't be late for the trip tomorrow,' said Bella. (next)
_____

3 'Have you heard the band's new album yet?' asked Kostas. (me)
_____

4 'I won't be at school next week,' said Mark. (says)
_____

5 'Will you be getting a new phone soon?' asked Harry. (whether)
_____

6 'My plane arrives at ten in the morning,' said Andrew. (tells)
_____

Urban legends

I can understand the meaning of different intonation patterns.

Listening Strategy

Speakers often use intonation to express their opinion or attitude about the statements they make. Pay attention to the speaker's tone of voice and the intonation they use to find out how they feel about their subject.

1 🎧 **2.08** Read the Listening Strategy. Then listen to the sentences and choose the tone of voice (a or b) each speaker uses.

1 Is that letter for me?
   a nervous   b surprised
2 No, that's not right. Let me show you.
   a angry   b patient
3 This is my seat.
   a certain   b uncertain
4 That makes me feel much better.
   a sarcastic   b enthusiastic
5 That didn't hurt at all.
   a surprised   b sarcastic
6 The film's quite good.
   a unsure   b enthusiastic
7 He's never on time.
   a irritated   b patient
8 This party's brilliant.
   a sarcastic   b enthusiastic

2 🎧 **2.08** Listen again and repeat the sentences, copying the tone of voice.

3 Now try saying the sentences in exercise 1 in the other tone of voice.

4 🎧 **2.09** Listen and repeat the different intonation patterns for statements.

1 Certain   3 Qualifying

   It's a great story.   It's a great story.

2 Uncertain   4 Sarcastic

   It's a great story.   It's a great story.

5 🎧 **2.10** Listen to these statements being said in two different ways. Number them 1 and 2 in the order you hear them. Practise saying them.

1 You like this kind of story.
   a certain ☐   b uncertain ☐
2 This is just what I wanted.
   a certain ☐   b sarcastic ☐
3 This isn't quite what I was expecting.
   a qualifying ☐   b certain ☐
4 He thinks it's a reasonable price.
   a qualifying ☐   b uncertain ☐
5 This steak is the best I've ever eaten.
   a sarcastic ☐   b certain ☐
6 That's really nice of him.
   a uncertain ☐   b sarcastic ☐

6 🎧 **2.11** Listen to the conversation. Choose the correct answers (a–d).

1 How does Max feel when he starts telling his story?
   a Reluctant to tell it.
   b Impatient with interruptions.
   c Unsure how the story goes.
   d Worried that it is too scary.
2 What is the story about?
   a A ghost.
   b A student who is lost.
   c What to do in bad weather.
   d The inhabitants of a village in Ireland.
3 What do the people listening think of the story?
   a It's gripping.
   b It's hilarious throughout.
   c It's annoying.
   d It's too similar to the first one.
4 What does Caro think of Max's comment about her?
   a She's really annoyed.
   b She admits that Max's comment could be right.
   c She criticises Max in self-defence.
   d She does not trust his opinion of her.
5 What does Max agree with Jill about?
   a That Caro is easily fooled.
   b That Caro is more good-natured than he is.
   c That Ian's story is better than his.
   d That Ian should buy the coffees.

Reporting verbs

I can report what people have said in a variety of ways.

1 Report the sentences using the reporting verbs below and *that*.

admit announce argue complain ~~deny~~ insist promise

1 Ian said 'I didn't leave the door open.'

Ian *denied that …* _____

2 'I think it would be dangerous to go out in this weather,' said George.

_____

3 Molly said, 'The traffic is so noisy that I can't hear myself think!'

_____

4 'I've decided to dye my hair orange,' said Mike.

_____

5 'Don't worry. I definitely won't tell anyone your secret,' Laura told me.

_____

6 Jackie said, 'This *can't* be my bag because it's the wrong colour.'

_____

7 'Yes, it was me who took the money,' said Fred.

_____

2 🎧 **2.12** **Listen and match the speakers with the reported speech.**

a She complained that the weather was too hot. _____

b She agreed that the weather was too hot. _____

c She explained that she would be late. _____

d She promised that she wouldn't be late. _____

e She denied that she was ill. _____

f She insisted that she was ill. _____

g She argued that it was too expensive. _____

h She agreed that it was too expensive. _____

3 **Write the words in the correct order to make sentences.**

1 to / for / invited / lunch / them / they / us / join

_____

2 helping / escape / to / denied / thieves / he / the

_____

3 into / on / lift / she / me / insisted / town / giving / a

_____

4 that / picnic / have / suggested / should / a / Jo / we

_____

5 Ned / losing / me / tickets / blamed / for / our

_____

6 tomorrow / that / to / me / she / promised / lend / DVD

_____

7 advised / go / not / doctor / running / the / him / to

_____

8 answer / that / didn't / admitted / she / Nina / the / know

_____

4 **Correct the underlined mistakes in the sentences. Use the correct reporting structures.**

1 She begged him not telling anyone what he'd heard.

_____

2 I suggested to meet him outside the cinema at eight.

_____

3 Belinda reminded me not forgetting the festival tickets.

_____

4 Anna recommended us to try the new burger bar in town.

_____

5 The teacher accused Jon to cheat in the test.

_____

6 Suzie apologised of not remembering to invite me.

_____

5 **Complete the sentences with a preposition if necessary and the correct form of the verb in brackets.**

1 Nick boasted _____ (come) top in the test.

2 Our teacher forbade us _____ (use) a dictionary.

3 My dad criticised me _____ (spend) too much.

4 His neighbour demanded _____ (he / turn down) his music.

5 She warned us _____ (not / stay) in that part of town.

6 He confessed _____ (sell) stolen goods.

7 I proposed _____ (we / find) somewhere to have a coffee.

8 Clara insisted _____ (give) them a hand with the cooking.

6 **Report the dialogue in your notebook using appropriate reporting verbs. There may be more than one answer.**

Greg Hi, Katya. I'm so sorry I didn't come to your barbecue yesterday.

Katya Actually, I was quite upset about it, Greg.

Greg It really wasn't my fault!

Katya I won't listen to any more of your lies, Greg.

Greg But I couldn't come because I broke my wrist and had to go to hospital!

Katya Oh, I see … Well, why don't you come over this afternoon?

Greg Great – and I'll definitely be there this time!

Katya OK. Oh, and don't forget to bring my birthday present with you!

Nouns and dependent prepositions
I can use nouns and dependent prepositions.

1 Match the sentences halves.

1 Nowadays there is a constant demand ☐
2 Do you have any objections ☐
3 Many people have a preference ☐
4 It's unlikely that the existence ☐
5 It's easy to develop an addiction ☐
6 Does anyone think our dependence ☐
7 The 1950s Space Age had a great effect ☐

a to inviting Emma for dinner?
b on computers nowadays is dangerous?
c on people's belief in aliens.
d for watching sci-fi rather than fantasy films.
e to video games if you play them too often.
f for better and faster technology.
g of life on other planets will ever be proved.

2 Complete the text with the words below.

belief   difference   evidence   increase   interest
need   obsession   reason

A few years ago, a National Geographic Society poll revealed that 36% of Americans (about 190 million people) believe in aliens, while only 17% do not, and the remaining 47% are undecided. The figures may be surprising, but people have had an ¹_____ in aliens since the late 1940s. A ²_____ in flying saucers, backed up by apparent ³_____ of these alien spaceships in the form of grainy black and white photos, soon turned into an ⁴_____ , with people claiming to have actually made contact with beings from outer space. More recently, there has been an ⁵_____ in this fascination with extraterrestrial life forms, thanks to detailed video footage 'proof' (created with high-quality 3-D computer software). It's hard to explain the ⁶_____ for this continued fascination; to many people, there seems to be little ⁷_____ between thinking UFOs exist and believing in magic. Perhaps it's just that we have always had the ⁸_____ for a little mystery in our lives.

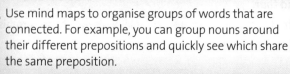

VOCAB BOOST!

Use mind maps to organise groups of words that are connected. For example, you can group nouns around their different prepositions and quickly see which share the same preposition.

3 Read the *Vocab boost!* box. Then complete the mind maps with the correct prepositions.

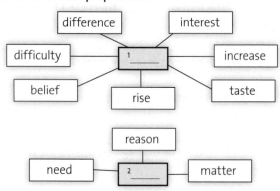

difference   interest
difficulty   1 _____   increase
belief   rise   taste

reason
need   2 _____   matter

4 Complete the sentences with the correct prepositions.

1 Is there really no possibility _____ you changing your mind?
2 This is probably a matter _____ the police.
3 There's a big difference _____ price between taking the bus and getting a taxi.
4 Is your taste _____ clothes the same as your friends'?
5 There's been a sharp rise _____ temperatures this month.
6 The police didn't find any evidence _____ a break-in.

5 Use a dictionary and correct the mistakes with prepositions in the sentences. Tick the two sentences that do not contain any mistakes.

1 No one expected the band to rise in fame so quickly.
_____

2 My cousin's gap year gave her a real taste for travel.
_____

3 Bill and his girlfriend have had a difference in opinion and aren't speaking. _____

4 You look very pale – is something the matter of you?
_____

5 Customers have recently been experiencing difficulty in using this website. _____

6 There's no point of getting upset about it. _____

6 Complete the sentences with the correct preposition and your own ideas.

1 I've never understood the point _____ .
2 Where I live, there's been a rise _____ .
3 Most of my friends have an interest _____ .
4 I wish we could find a solution _____ .
5 I hardly ever have trouble _____ .
6 I'd love to prove the existence _____ .
7 Nowadays, there's very little demand _____ .

Media wars

I can understand an article that discusses different types of media.

Revision: Student's Book page 80

1 Replace the underlined words with the correct form of the phrasal verbs.

find out   hole up   let on   make out   play on
set up   take in   zoom in on

1 I can't believe you were <u>deceived</u> by his tricks!
2 The criminals <u>established</u> false bank accounts.
3 I hate advertising that <u>takes advantage of</u> our fears.
4 Mark <u>told us</u> that he was planning a surprise for Anna.
5 The police <u>discovered</u> what the criminals were planning.
6 The media <u>paid special attention to</u> the government's military plans.
7 He <u>claimed</u> that he was rich, but it wasn't true.
8 The bank robbers were <u>hiding</u> in a friend's house.

2 Read the text. What does the real story behind *The War of the Worlds* show us?

Reading Strategy

In a multiple-choice task:

1 Questions always appear in the same order as the information about them in the text.
2 The correct answer will match the meaning of what you find in the text, but it isn't usually expressed in the same words.
3 When there's a question about the main idea of the text or the author's opinion, it usually appears last.

3 Read the Reading Strategy and the text again and choose the correct answers (a–d).

1 The announcer on the radio play in 1934
   a said American farmers were being attacked.
   b suggested that what he was saying was difficult to believe.
   c explained that America was invading Mars.
   d was suffering from a panic attack.

2 HG Wells's famous novel
   a was adapted for the radio.
   b deceived millions of people.
   c became famous in 1934.
   d was about media manipulation.

3 Newspapers didn't like the radio because
   a it was more exciting.
   b it controlled people.
   c it worried people.
   d it was a rival for income.

4 The stories in the newspapers about the play
   a were based on information from another radio station.
   b have been forgotten about today.
   c are only being questioned today.
   d explained what really happened.

5 The writer wants to show that
   a people can be made to believe that they are being attacked by aliens.
   b there wasn't enough advertising for both the radio and newspapers in the 1930s.
   c the radio and newspapers are enemies.
   d the media can create a legend that is not true.

> 'Ladies and gentlemen, I have a grave announcement to make. Incredible as it may seem . . . those strange beings who landed in the Jersey farmlands tonight are . . . an invading army from the planet Mars.'

Orson Welles reading *The War of the Worlds*

This announcement in 1934 supposedly scared a million Americans into believing that thousands of their fellow citizens were fighting for their lives against giant aliens. It came from a radio play, read by Orson Welles, that was based on HG Wells's famous 1898 novel *The War of the Worlds*, and it has become an American media legend. However, as we all know, legends are rarely based on the truth.

The arrival of the radio in the 1930s provided people with an exciting new channel of communication – but it also provided newspapers with unwanted competition. Throughout the decade, more and more people had come to rely on the radio for news, and newspapers had been losing income from advertising. In addition, many people were worried about its possible use as a form of mind control. *The War of the Worlds* gave newspapers the perfect excuse to exploit these fears and attack their rival as irresponsible. The day after the play was broadcast, newspaper front pages claimed the radio play had caused panic across the country, with people rioting and even committing suicide. However, the stories were fabricated and completely false. Recent research has shown that most people were listening to another radio station that evening, and there are no records of mass hysteria.

The newspapers of the time wanted the public to believe that new technology could not be trusted, and they did an extremely good job. For decades, the story of people's reaction to *The War of the Worlds* was seen as an example of how the media could cause panic. It is only now that researchers are realising that the whole episode is an example of something even more worrying: it shows how the media could fabricate and maintain a lie for nearly a century.

Presentation

I can discuss the link between technology and crime.

GANGS STEALING 17 CARS A DAY IN HIGH-TECH SPATE OF 'KEYLESS' THEFTS ON LONDON'S STREETS

Look at the photo and the headline. Then talk for about one minute about how technology has led to an increase in some crimes, but also to new ways of fighting crime. Think about:
- the internet.
- theft of expensive items.
- surveillance and anti-theft measures.

1 Read the task above. Then choose the correct option, a or b, in the sentences below.

1 The headline refers to how technology can
  a cause certain crimes to increase.
  b help to fight crime.
2 The photo shows how technology can
  a cause certain crimes to increase.
  b help to fight crime.

2 🎧 2.13 Listen to a student doing the task. Which of the topics below does he mention?

artificial intelligence   car crime   computers   credit cards
email scams   mobile phones   television

> **Speaking Strategy**
> Avoid speaking in short, single sentences. Try to develop your statements with extra information, details and examples. Learn a variety of phrases for introducing them.

3 Read the Speaking Strategy. Then complete the phrases for introducing extra information and examples with the words below.

instance   kind   that   way   what   words

a One example of _____ would be ...
b So, for _____ , ...
c _____ I mean by that is ...
d The _____ of thing I'm talking about is ...
e In other _____ , ...
f Or to put it another _____ , ...

4 🎧 2.13 Listen again. Complete these sentences from the student's presentation with the correct phrases from exercise 3. Write a–f.

1 ___ an email saying you've won millions in a lottery.
2 ___ cars are much harder to steal these days.
3 ___ criminals can use their knowledge of technology to commit crimes.
4 ___ people don't commit crimes if there are cameras about.
5 ___ crime doesn't stop; it just moves to another area.
6 ___ the mobile phone.

A social media campaign using the hashtag #nomakeupselfie has raised £8 million for charity in just six days. Huge numbers of women, including many celebrities, have posted photos of themselves wearing no make-up and nominated friends to do the same. At the same time, they encourage their friends to donate money to Cancer Research UK. However, the campaign was started by an individual, not by Cancer Research, and shows how social media can be a force for good.

HALF of all young people say cyberbullying is part of everyday life as majority of parents admit they are scared for their children online

Look at the news report and the headline. Then talk for about one minute about how social media can make people's lives better or worse. Think about:
- friends and networks.
- cyberbullying and lies.
- petitions and online campaigns.

5 Read the task above. Then make notes under the headings below.

Examples of how friendships are strengthened
_____
_____

Examples of cyberbullying / lies
_____
_____

Examples of how social media campaigns can make a difference
_____
_____
_____

6 Now do the task using your notes from exercise 5. Remember to include phrases from exercise 3.

7H Writing
A story
I can write a story on a given topic.

Preparation

1 Read the task and the story below. Match time expressions a–f with gaps 1–4 in the text. There are two extra time expressions.

a After a few more minutes
b It all started one day last term
c Looking back
d On the day of the ceremony
e The following year
f Within two or three weeks

> Write a story about an occasion when somebody started a rumour which caused problems.

2 Answer the questions. Which paragraph (A–D) contains:

1 the main event in the story? ___
2 speculation about how somebody felt? ___
3 information about how it all started? ___
4 information about different students' plans? ___

3 Rewrite the sentences so that they have a similar meaning. Start with the words in brackets.

1 I wanted to be honest with them. (What I wanted ...)

_____

2 Her opinions hurt my feelings. (What hurt ...)

_____

3 The possibility of failing the exam worried her. (What worried her ...)

_____

4 We needed more time. (What we needed ...)

_____

5 I really wanted to take the exam again. (What I really ...)

_____

Writing Guide

> **Writing Strategy**
> When you write a story:
> - you can choose to narrate the events in the first person (using *I*) or the third person (using *he, she, it, they*).
> - use paragraphs to show that events happened at different times.
> - include time expressions (e.g. *a week later, soon afterwards*) to move the story forwards.
> - describe how people felt and reacted to the events.

> Write a story about an occasion when somebody caused problems by cheating.

A ¹___ when we heard that a special guest was going to speak to the school at the summer prize-giving ceremony. I don't know who started the rumour, but people started to say that this guest was going to be the actor Matt Damon. Of course, this was very exciting news!

B ²___ , nearly everybody in the school had heard the rumour. What is amazing is that nearly everybody thought it was true! People started to plan what they were going to do when they saw Matt Damon. Some wanted autographs; others wanted to take selfies. One student even set up a live stream on the internet!

C ³___ , the atmosphere in the school was electric. As we waited in the school hall, we whispered excitedly. Then the doors opened and the head teacher walked in with the special guest: the local police commander. We were stunned – and extremely disappointed! We listened while he gave a speech, but when the head teacher asked for questions at the end, nobody said a word. The only question we had in our minds was: where's Matt?

D ⁴___ , I feel quite sorry for the police commander. He didn't know that we were hoping for Matt Damon, but he probably sensed our disappointment. I still don't know who started the rumour, but I sometimes wonder if they feel bad about it.

4 Read the Writing Strategy and the task above. Make notes below.

Paragraph 1: Set the scene. How did it begin?

_____

Paragraph 2: Lead-up to the main event.

_____

Paragraph 3: The main event. How did people feel / react?

_____

Paragraph 4: Ending / Looking back

_____

5 Write your story using your notes from exercise 4.

> **CHECK YOUR WORK**
> **Have you ...**
> ☐ organised the events into paragraphs?
> ☐ included adjectives to describe feelings and reactions?
> ☐ used appropriate time expressions?
> ☐ checked your spelling and grammar?

Review Unit 7

Vocabulary

1 Complete the sentences with the verbs below.

cheat   disguise   exaggerate   fool
make   photoshop   swear   tell

1 Why don't you just _____ an excuse if you don't want to go to the party?
2 Don't _____ ! You can't have walked 100 km!
3 I _____ that I didn't take your watch. It wasn't me!
4 If you _____ , your test paper won't be accepted.
5 Mary's story didn't _____ me. I knew she was lying.
6 That picture can't be real. Did you _____ it?
7 Tom couldn't _____ the fact that he'd been crying.
8 _____ me the truth! Did you, or did you not, delete that file from my computer?

Mark: ⬜ / 8

2 Complete the sentences with the adjective form of the nouns below.

bias   ethic   hypocrite   manipulation   truth   trust

1 If you aren't _____ with me about your part in the incident, I won't be able to trust you again.
2 That shop is looking for a _____ person to look after their accounts.
3 You're _____ about the referee's decision because you want your team to win.
4 Is it _____ to buy expensive electronic devices when the people that make them are paid so little?
5 Lola's rather _____. I don't like the way she tries to control me and my other friends.
6 It would be _____ of me to accept Ruby's invitation when I don't actually like her.

Mark: ⬜ / 6

Word Skills

3 Choose the correct prepositions (a–c).

1 People are worried about the increase ___ knife crime.
   a of   b in   c on
2 Sugary drinks can have a devastating effect ___ a person's health.
   a in   b to   c on
3 Most of the students expressed a preference ___ postponing the exam for a week.
   a for   b with   c to
4 My main objection ___ getting a part-time job is that I won't have enough time to study.
   a of   b to   c between

5 Rosie's obsession ___ her favourite band takes her all over the country.
   a for   b in   c with
6 Until now, nobody has been able to prove the existence ___ life on other planets.
   a of   b for   c to
7 The difference ___ Asian and African elephants is that the former have smaller ears.
   a in   b with   c between
8 There is an urgent need ___ effective measures to house the world's refugees.
   a for   b with   c in

Mark: ⬜ / 8

4 Complete the text with the phrasal verbs below.

find out   let on   make out   play on   taken in   zoom in

Liars often try to [1]_____ our ignorance and they put on an act in order to be believed. The best way to [2]_____ if a person is lying is to [3]_____ on their body language. They tend to [4]_____ that they're being sincere by looking very deeply into your eyes. Don't be [5]_____ by this and listen carefully to what they're saying. They won't admit their guilt directly, but subconsciously they will often [6]_____ that they're lying by using too many negatives: 'I swear that I didn't use your tablet. Never. Not once.'

Mark: ⬜ / 6

Grammar

5 Rewrite the sentences using reported speech.

1 'I'll never wear this outfit again.'
   Monica said _____.
2 'I don't believe you.'
   My dad told my sister _____.
3 'I've been talking to Frank.'
   Susanna tells me _____.
4 'You mustn't tell anyone.'
   Harry told me _____.
5 'I'll give you an answer tomorrow.'
   Jenny told Tom _____.
6 'I was at a friend's house yesterday.'
   Lisa said _____.

Mark: ⬜ / 6

6 Rewrite the questions using reported speech.

1 'Did you see the football match yesterday?'
   Jimmy asked me _____ .

2 'You've ordered the pizzas, haven't you?'
   I asked Eddie _____ .

3 'What languages do you speak?'
   The tourist asked me _____ .

4 'You're going out later, aren't you?'
   My dad asked me _____ .

5 'Do you like Indian food?' 'Yes, I do.'
   They asked me _____ .

6 'Where does your brother work?'
   I asked Emma _____ .

7 'Were you late for school this morning?'
   My mum asked my sister _____ .

8 'Are you tired?' 'No, I'm not.'
   We asked him _____ .

Mark: ___ / 8

7 Complete the sentences with the correct form of the verbs in brackets.

1 Kevin insisted on _____ for our meal, although I was quite happy to share the bill. (pay)

2 We congratulated my uncle on _____ the photo competition. (win)

3 You promised _____ anyone about our secret place. (not / tell)

4 I've agreed _____ with our school's next fund-raising event. (help)

5 My grandmother apologised for _____ me a birthday card. (not / send)

6 Charlotte's friends encouraged her _____ the drama group. (join)

7 The waiter recommended _____ two portions of chips instead of four. (order)

8 The doctor advised me _____ basketball for a week. (not / play)

Mark: ___ / 8

Use of English

8 Complete the sentences with the correct form of the words in brackets. Use up to six words, including the words in brackets. Do not change the order of the words in brackets.

1 I just confronted my friend and she has finally _____ (admit / take) my laptop yesterday.

2 The student tried to _____ (pass / essay) her own, despite having copied it.

3 After collecting them at school, Stephen _____ (lie / mother) his exam results.

4 In his letter, he explains his _____ (reasons / oppose) the new leadership.

5 I don't understand your _____ (interest / read) my text messages.

6 I _____ (offer / accompany) my sister to the doctor's yesterday.

7 This morning, my mother _____ (remind / pack) my bag for my holiday.

8 Everybody is _____ (blame / break) the window, but it wasn't my fault.

9 I _____ (apologise / forget) her name, but she just laughed.

10 They couldn't _____ (deny / vandalise) the bus stop because they were caught red-handed.

Mark: ___ / 10

Total: ___ / 60

I can ...

Read the statements. Think about your progress and tick one of the boxes.

★ = I need more practice.   ★★★ = No problem!

★★ = I sometimes find this difficult.

	★	★★	★★★
I can talk about telling the truth and lies.			
I can report what people have said and asked.			
I can understand the meaning of different intonation patterns.			
I can report what people have said in a variety of ways.			
I can use nouns and dependent prepositions.			
I can understand an article that discusses different types of media.			
I can discuss the link between technology and crime.			
I can write a story on a given topic.			

8 Change the world

Vocabulary

A Protest

I can talk about local and global issues.

1 Match 1–7 with a–g.

1	shout	a	a demonstration
2	hold up	b	a petition
3	go on	c	speeches
4	listen to	d	a rally
5	hold	e	inequality
6	sign	f	slogans
7	demonstrate against	g	placards

2 🎧 **2.14 Listen to a conversation between Ewan and Emily. Which of the things below do they mention?**

famine   globalisation   global warming   homelessness
immigration   unemployment

3 🎧 **2.14 Listen again. Are the sentences true (T) or false (F)?**

1 Emily is going on a rally this weekend. ☐
2 Ewan signed a petition against climate change. ☐
3 Emily went on a march against a new shopping centre. ☐
4 Ewan doesn't think protesting will make politicians do anything. ☐
5 Emily thinks companies might act more responsibly if people stop buying their products. ☐
6 Emily thinks that protesting against something is useful. ☐

4 Match the words below with the situations.

corruption   disease   global warming   homelessness
terrorism   unemployment

1 We interviewed Tom, who had been living on the streets for a year. _____
2 All Americans will remember 11 September 2001, when two planes crashed into the World Trade Center. _____
3 Ebola, which is a virus, has killed thousands of people in West Africa. _____
4 A politician from New York, who accepted money from companies in return for changing policies to benefit them, has been sent to prison. _____
5 My brother, Jack, who has got a degree, still hasn't been able to find a job. _____
6 The weather in the Caribbean, where there have been extremely strong hurricanes, has been the worst on record. _____

5 Complete the sentences with the nouns below.

censorship   famine   gender inequality   immigration
nuclear weapons   racism

1 Banning controversial books is an example of _____ .
2 The British population has increased because of _____ and 12% of UK residents were born outside the country.
3 Although there is less _____ today, African Americans still find it more difficult to find jobs than white Americans.
4 Considering how much food we throw away in developed countries, it's a crime that _____ continues to affect a large part of the world's population.
5 More and more countries have _____ , and that makes the world more dangerous, not safer.
6 Although _____ has been tackled in places like universities, there is discrimination against women in many places.

6 Complete the text with the correct form of the verbs below.

campaign   organise   send   stand   support   vote

I've decided to ¹_____ on behalf of an independent candidate for next year's elections for President. I don't ²_____ the policies of either candidate from the two main parties although in the past I have ³_____ for both parties. I think it's very brave to ⁴_____ for election when you don't have a big party to help you, and that's why I'm helping to ⁵_____ meetings and rallies so people can hear what our candidate has to say. I'm also ⁶_____ emails to the media to invite them to meet him. It's going to be hard work, but if we don't try, nothing will change!

Second and third conditional

I can use second and third conditionals.

1 Correct the mistakes in the second conditional sentences. Tick the correct sentences.

> knew
> If I ~~know~~ the answer, I would tell you. ☐

1 He can save money if he didn't buy so many clothes. ☐
2 If it snows tomorrow, we might not have to go to school. ☐
3 I would listen to your parents' advice if I were you. ☐
4 If Dan were older, he would be able to ride a motorbike. ☐
5 She could go to university if she would study harder. ☐
6 If they aren't so tired, they'd come out with us later. ☐
7 Pat would learn to play the guitar if he has more time. ☐

2 Complete the third conditional sentences with the correct form of the verbs below.

fall   go   help   not leave   lend   not remember   see   tell

1 If he'd finished his homework, he would _____ to bed earlier.
2 I could _____ you some money if you'd asked me.
3 She might _____ if I hadn't reminded her.
4 If they _____ Sam recently, they would have invited him to the concert.
5 We could _____ him if we'd known he was in trouble.
6 If the bus _____ on time, we might have missed the start of the match.
7 You could have hurt yourself if you _____ off that ladder!
8 If Jenny didn't trust you, she wouldn't _____ you her secret.

3 Complete the text with the correct form of the verbs in brackets.

The internet has transformed campaigning. Campaign organisers couldn't publicise their campaigns if we ¹_____ (have) the internet. Many protests and demonstrations simply ²_____ (not happen) if the public hadn't learned about the campaigns through social media. Many people say they would only get involved in a campaign if they ³_____ (see) their online friends were too. Support for direct action such as protests ⁴_____ (not be) so great if the organisers couldn't send details about where and when so quickly and to so many people. And in the past, if there had been a major news story like a demonstration, it ⁵_____ (take) a whole day to be reported; today, if you ⁶_____ (post) images from your smartphone, they could be online almost instantly for everyone to see.

4 Choose the correct words to complete the sentences.

1 **Supposing / Unless** we didn't have antibiotics – life would be very different.
2 She wouldn't have voted for him **supposing / unless** she really thought he could make a difference.
3 **Unless / Even if** we got rid of nuclear weapons, there would still always be wars.
4 **Unless / Supposing** everyone thought their vote didn't count? Nobody would vote!
5 I would never vote for that party, **supposing / even if** I were old enough.
6 **Unless / Supposing** I hadn't got lost, I wouldn't have found such a beautiful view!

5 Choose the correct options (a–c) to complete the text.

> How would you feel if you ¹___ the right to vote as an adult? Or ²___ you lived in a country where it was illegal <u>not</u> to vote – how would you feel then? In many countries where voting isn't compulsory, the number of people doing so has fallen dramatically. If their ancestors ³___ that fewer than 60% of the public would vote during the US presidential elections, they ⁴___ have fought so hard for that right. But there are 22 nations around the world where you'd have to vote in an election, ⁵___ you didn't want to. And if you lived in Australia, you could be fined ⁶___ you voted!

1 a hadn't   b didn't have   c hadn't had
2 a unless   b even if   c supposing
3 a had known   b knew   c would know
4 a couldn't   b might not   c hadn't
5 a supposing   b unless   c even if
6 a unless   b even if   c supposing

6 Rewrite the sentences in the second or third conditional so that they have the same meaning. Use the words in brackets.

1 She didn't receive the email so she missed the meeting. (if)
_____

2 He could beg me to go, but I'd still refuse! (even)
_____

3 Because I'm not from Greece, I don't speak Greek. (were)
_____

4 What would you do first if you were the President? (supposing)
_____

5 My computer's broken, so I can't check my emails. (could)
_____

6 If he hadn't thought it was really important, he wouldn't have gone on the demonstration. (unless)
_____

Listening

Hashtag activism

I can use discourse markers to help predict what will be said next.

'I'm Charlotte. I'm seventeen and I live in Bristol, which is, ¹___ , one of the coolest cities in the south-west of England. My friends and I saw reports of the national anti-austerity demonstration in London – ²___ , where people were protesting against the threatened cuts in welfare from the new government. It was too far for us to travel, but ³___ we wished we could have been there. And then one of my friends said, '⁴___ , why don't we organise one here?' We put up an invitation on Facebook to all of our friends. ⁵___ , we hadn't done anything like it before so we didn't know what to expect. But it just grew from there, and on the day, five thousand people turned up to demonstrate! It was a completely amazing experience.

⁶___ , a lot of great things have come out of that one Facebook page. ⁷___ , we are now collecting food for local food banks and women's shelters. We're only young, but ⁸___ , with Facebook, we're effective!'

1 Choose the correct linkers (a–c) to complete the text.

	a	b	c
1	all the same	incidentally	for instance
2	you know	nevertheless	well
3	all the same	by the way	for instance
4	Well	Nevertheless	As I was saying
5	Mind you	For instance	Talking of which
6	All the same	By the way	However
7	Still	Incidentally	For instance
8	even so	for instance	by the way

2 🎧 2.15 Listen and check your answers to exercise 1.

Listening Strategy

As you listen, pay special attention to discourse markers (linking phrases), which connect pieces of information to each other. For example, *however* introduces a contrast, whereas *for instance* introduces an example.

3 Read the Listening Strategy and match the sentence halves.

1 I am not sure who to vote for. ☐
2 We couldn't go to London to demonstrate. ☐
3 I don't really understand how Twitter works. ☐
4 My sister went on a protest march at the weekend. ☐
5 Scientists say it will be difficult to reverse global warming. ☐
6 Journalists are sometimes difficult to trust. ☐

a Nevertheless, I will try to use it.
b Even so, that's no excuse not to do it at all.
c Still, we managed to protest effectively in other ways.
d Talking of protests, did you sign that petition about equal rights?
e By the way, did you know that Matt is studying journalism at university?
f All the same, it would be better to try to do something about it.

4 🎧 2.16 Listen and check your answers.

5 🎧 2.17 Listen and match speakers 1–4 with sentences A–E. There is one extra sentence.

This speaker:

A talks about a particular online protest and how it evolved into something else. ☐
B explains that the perceived lack of interest in politics in the young is not accurate. ☐
C took action to encourage young people's interest in politics. ☐
D proves that social media is essential in political campaigns. ☐
E feels that there is no division between social media campaigning and other forms of protest. ☐

8D Grammar
Mixed conditionals
I can use mixed conditionals.

1 Write the words in brackets in the correct order to form mixed conditional sentences. Add a comma in the correct place.

1 If (know / you'd / the answer / you'd / listened).
   If _____

2 If (weren't / I'd / have / raining / it / walked).
   If _____

3 If (he / have / Lucas / older / voted / could / were).
   If _____

4 If (chips / have / hungry / I'd / those / was / eaten / I).
   If _____

5 If (champions / might / scored / they'd / they / be / the).
   If _____

6 If (you / I / have / that / were / done / wouldn't / I).
   If _____

2 Choose the correct options (a–c) to complete the mixed conditional sentences.

1 If Tony ___ the lottery, he would be rich.
   a wins   **b** had won   **c** would win

2 Life ___ difficult if they hadn't invented electricity!
   a would be   **b** had been   **c** was

3 If you'd burned the cake, we ___ eat it.
   a can't   **b** weren't able to   **c** couldn't

4 If Zoe were braver, she ___ for Ed's phone number.
   a might have asked   **b** might asking   **c** might not ask

5 We'd have gone to school if it ___ the weekend.
   a weren't   **b** hadn't been   **c** isn't

6 If I ___ your advice, I'd have asked for it.
   a want   **b** would want   **c** wanted

7 If I hadn't seen the news, I ___ about the accident.
   a didn't know   **b** wouldn't know   **c** hadn't known

3 Complete the mixed conditional sentences with up to five words, including the correct form of the words in brackets. Do not change the order of the words.

1 I would be sad if (I / never / meet) you!
   _____

2 If Max hadn't run so fast, (he / not / exhausted).
   _____

3 They wouldn't be nervous about the exam (they / study / harder).
   _____

4 (you / be / poor) you'd spent all your money yesterday.
   _____

5 If Lily had used suncream on the beach, (she / burned / now)!
   _____

6 I would have written to you if (I / know / address).
   _____

4 Complete the email with one word in each gap to make mixed conditional sentences.

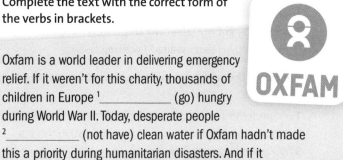

To: daisy@email.com

Hi Daisy

Did you watch Comic Relief on TV last night? I might ¹_____ missed it if my mum ²_____ such a huge fan – if she ³_____ reminded me it was on, I'd be really annoyed! Of course, it ⁴_____ have been so funny if the people taking part weren't really famous. And the amount of money they've raised wouldn't ⁵_____ so much if the public hadn't joined in as well. Anyway, it was great fun and I watched it to the end – but I wouldn't be so tired today if I ⁶_____ gone to bed at my usual time!

See you soon, Artur

5 Complete the text with the correct form of the verbs in brackets.

Oxfam is a world leader in delivering emergency relief. If it weren't for this charity, thousands of children in Europe ¹_____ (go) hungry during World War II. Today, desperate people ²_____ (not have) clean water if Oxfam hadn't made this a priority during humanitarian disasters. And if it ³_____ (not be) for Oxfam, the NGO ActionAid might not exist either; there wouldn't be so much pressure on governments to provide healthcare and education and to combat climate change if these charities ⁴_____ (not develop). But Oxfam might not be so successful nowadays if it ⁵_____ (not recognise) the importance of linking business with charity. Oxfam employs thousands of people worldwide, but it couldn't have become the UK's biggest high-street seller of second-hand books if it ⁶_____ (not be) also for the thousands of volunteers who give their time working in these important charity shops.

Verb patterns

I am aware of and can use different verb patterns.

1 Write the words in the correct order to make sentences.

1 a / to / have / take / airport / We'll / taxi / us / the
2 teacher / The / again / us / our / test / made / do
3 you / Would / later / prefer / call / to / me / back / ?
4 stop / war / was / The / to / president / made / the
5 someone / bicycle / your / Did / fix / get / you / to / ?
6 check / cut / You'd / doctor / have / better / a / that
7 school / making / walk / Vic's / Is / mum / him / to / ?

2 Choose the correct words to complete the sentences.

1 We're having our dog **looked** / **looking** after by a neighbour.
2 I've left the keys **hidden** / **hiding** under the mat.
3 The film will keep you **guessing** / **guessed** to the end!
4 Don't leave that candle **burning** / **burned** when you go to bed.
5 They got their house **painted** / **painting** by a friend.
6 I don't want that painting **throwing** / **thrown** away.
7 I've finally got my tablet **working** / **worked** again!
8 Rob found his sister **waited** / **waiting** outside.

3 Complete the sentences with the correct form of the verb in brackets.

1 I'd prefer you _____ (tell) me the complete truth.
2 I found this bottle _____ (float) in the sea.
3 My parents can't get anyone _____ (buy) our flat.
4 I had the garage _____ (service) my car.
5 Would you like your meal _____ (serve) with chips or salad?
6 I think we should ask him _____ (help) us.
7 Tony was made _____ (apologise).

4 Choose the correct options (a–c) to complete the text.

Most people would prefer the world's problems ¹___ through non-violent actions and there have been many successful peaceful protests over the years. One of the most famous took place when a 42-year-old African American woman changed the course of history – just by sitting on a bus. In 1955 in the United States, black people ²___ to give up their seats on public transport for white passengers. So one day, when a white man boarded a full bus which Rosa Parks was on, the driver tried to get four black people ³___ their seats. The law at the time said that he couldn't have a white person ⁴___ while black people had seats. Rosa Parks wanted this law ⁵___ , so she refused to give up her seat for the white man. Not surprisingly for that time, the authorities had the police ⁶___ her. But her actions made the rest of the USA ⁷___ notice, and this was the start of non-violent mass protests in support of civil rights.

7053

1 **a** solved	**b** to be solved	**c** to solve
2 **a** were made	**b** were making	**c** make
3 **a** leaving	**b** left	**c** to leave
4 **a** to stand	**b** standing	**c** stood
5 **a** changed	**b** changing	**c** change
6 **a** to arrest	**b** arrest	**c** arresting
7 **a** take	**b** to take	**c** taken

5 Complete the second sentence so that it means the same as the first.

1 I want us to forget our silly argument.
   I want our _____ .
2 They should have their photos taken by a professional.
   They should have a _____ .
3 I don't think anyone will steal your bag.
   I don't think you'll have _____ .
4 The police made him prove his age.
   He was _____ .
5 I'd rather we met tomorrow evening.
   I'd prefer us _____ .
6 We couldn't make the man understand us.
   We couldn't get _____ .
7 She was made to leave the party by her mum.
   Her mum _____ .

> **VOCAB BOOST!**
>
> When you learn verb patterns, you'll see that dictionaries usually present them with *sb / sth*, for example, *get sb / sth to do sth*. You can record new verb patterns in this way, or you can write more meaningful or personal examples and highlight the verb pattern:
>
> My dad couldn't <u>get the car to start</u> this morning.
>
> I <u>was made to do</u> my maths homework again.

6 Read the *Vocab boost!* box. Then complete the sentences with your own ideas. Use verb patterns from this page. Circle the verb patterns in your sentences.

1 I hate being made _____ .
2 I plan to get my _____ .
3 I'd prefer my parents _____ .
4 I would never leave my _____ .
5 I sometimes have my _____ .
6 I've always wanted my _____ .
7 I once found my _____ .

The Help

I can understand an extract from an American novel.

The Help

Revision: Student's Book page 92

1 Complete the sentences with the phrasal verbs below.

got ahead   helps out   set up   squeeze in
stepped down   thinking up

1 Sam _____ by working hard and showing enthusiasm.

2 The doctor said he could _____ me _____ for a quick appointment at 11.45.

3 Andy has _____ as the head of the charity and he is going to work in politics instead.

4 My mum _____ the company ten years ago and it now employs over a hundred people.

5 Sara's always _____ crazy new ideas for vlogs that never work!

6 Harry _____ at the homeless centre by cooking in the kitchen two evenings a week.

2 You are going to read an extract from the novel *The Help*. The author writes dialogues using the language conventions of the southern states of the USA. Rewrite the sentences below in standard British English.

1 This what she been trying to ask me the past two weeks.

_____

2 "You think Miss Leefolt gone agree to that?"

_____

3 "... do that not sound kind a dangerous to you?"

_____

Reading Strategy

Read all the text once and then read the questions. Match any questions that are immediately obvious, and identify and note the parts of the text that contain the evidence for your answer. Then carefully read each section of the text again and look for the answers to the remaining questions.

3 Read the Reading Strategy. Match sections A–C in the extract with questions 1–6 below. Each section may be matched with more than one question.

Which section ...

1 gives examples of violent racism? ☐

2 talks about the number of interviews that Miss Skeeter wants to do? ☐

3 discusses the consequences of helping Miss Skeeter for the narrator? ☐

4 mentions Miss Skeeter realising that the situation is more difficult than she imagined? ☐

5 talks about not telling anyone about the plan? ☐

6 suggests that Miss Skeeter's behaviour is rude? ☐

Kathryn Stockett's novel *The Help* is set in the 1960s, a time when the Civil Rights movement is campaigning all across the USA for equal rights for African Americans. Skeeter Phelan, a white woman, wants to write a book to protest against the unfair treatment of African Americans – a book about the experiences of African American maids who work for white families. In this extract, Skeeter asks Aibileen, a black maid, if she can interview her.

A "What can I do for you?"

"I have an idea. Something I want to write about. But I need your help."

I let all my breath out. I like Miss Skeeter, but come on. Sure, a phone call would a been nice. She never would a just shown up on some white lady's step without calling. But no, she done plopped herself down like she got ever right to barge in on me at home.

"I want to interview you. About what it's like to work as a maid." (…)

"Like the Miss Myrna column?" I say, flat as a pan. "Bout cleaning?"

"Not like Miss Myrna. I'm talking about a book," she say and her eyes is big. She excited. "Stories about what it's like to work for a white family. What it's like to work for, say … Elizabeth."

B I turn and look at her. This what she been trying to ask me the past two weeks in Miss Leefolt kitchen. "You think Miss Leefolt gone agree to that? Me telling stories about her?"

Miss Skeeter's eyes drop down some. "Well, no. I was thinking we wouldn't tell her. I'll have to make sure the other maids will agree to keep it secret, too."

I scrunch up my forehead, just starting to get what she's asking. "Other maids?"

"I was hoping to get four or five. To really show what it's like to be a maid in Jackson." (…)

C She looks excited, like this is some kind of game. For a second, I think I might be more mad than I am tired.

"Miss Skeeter," I whisper, "do that not sound kind a dangerous to you?"

"Not if we're careful—"

"Shhh, please. Do you know what would happen to me if Miss Leefolt find out I talked behind her back?"

"We won't tell her, or anyone." She lowers her voice some, but not enough. "These will be private interviews."

I just stare at her. Is she crazy? "Did you hear about the colored boy this morning? One they beat with a tire iron for *accidentally* using the white bathroom?"

She just look at me, blink a little. "I know things are unstable but this is—"

"And my cousin Shinelle in Cauter County? They burn up her car cause she went *down* to the voting station."

"No one's ever written a book like this," she say, finally whispering, finally starting to understand, I guess. "We'd be breaking new ground. It's a brand-new perspective."

Collaborative task

I can discuss a question with a partner and work towards an agreement.

Imagine that you are discussing practical ways in which people can help to combat pollution. How effective is each of the five measures?

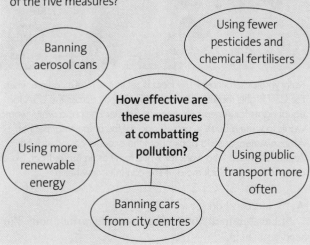

1 🎧 2.18 Read the task above and listen to two students doing the task. Answer the questions. Which three measures do the students agree will be particularly effective?

2 KEY PHRASES Match the sentence halves in each group below to make phrases.

Starting a discussion	
1 Shall we	**a** with ... , shall we? ☐
2 Let's begin	**b** by talking about ... ☐
3 We could start	**c** start with ... ? ☐
Expressing an opinion	
4 I'm of the	**d** chief consideration is ... ☐
5 For me, the	**e** strongly that ... ☐
6 Personally, I would	**f** say that ... ☐
7 I feel quite	**g** opinion that ... ☐
Adding an opinion	
8 Not	**h** only that, ... ☐
9 Yes, and another	**i** also believe that ... ☐
10 Good point. And I	**j** thing. ... ☐
Agreeing and disagreeing	
11 Absolutely. I couldn't	**k** some extent. However, ... ☐
12 I'm with	**l** agree more. ☐
13 Yes, I think	**m** you on that. ☐
14 That's true to	**n** you're right. ☐
15 I'm not sure I	**o** different view on that. ☐
16 I take a rather	**p** how I see it. ☐
17 That's not quite	**q** agree. ☐

3 🎧 2.18 Listen again and tick the phrases in exercise 2 that you hear.

4 🎧 2.19 Listen to students doing the second part of the task. Which two measures do they choose?

5 KEY PHRASES Read the Speaking Strategy. Then complete the phrases with the words below.

agree   Can   come   interrupt   moment   need
only   reach   settled   think   What   view

Involving your partner
Would you ¹_____ with that? ☐
... , don't you ²_____ ? ☐
³_____ we agree that ... ? ☐
What's your ⁴_____ on that? ☐
⁵_____ do you think about ... ? ☐

Interrupting
Sorry to ⁶_____ , but ... ☐
Hang on a ⁷_____ . I think ... ☐
Yes, and not ⁸_____ that, ... ☐

Reaching an agreement
So, shall we ⁹_____ a decision? ☐
We need to ¹⁰_____ to a decision. ☐
We ¹¹_____ to decide what / which ... ☐
That's ¹²_____ , then. ☐

6 🎧 2.19 Listen again and tick the phrases in exercise 5 that you hear.

7 Look at the task in exercise 1 again and the options below. Write notes about how effective each measure is.

Closing fossil-fuelled power stations

Flying less

Not littering

How effective are these measures at combatting pollution?

Using electric and hybrid cars

Joining an environmental organisation

_____
_____
_____
_____

8 Which two measures will you choose? Make a note of your choices and your reasons.

_____
_____
_____

9 Now do the task using your notes from exercises 7 and 8.

8H

Writing
A report
I can write a report about a local issue.

Preparation

1 Read the task and the report below. How many measures does the writer:

a assess? ___ **b** suggest? ___

> Last year, your town council took measures to make your town cleaner and greener. The council would like to hear your views on the measures they have taken and also any suggestions for future improvements.
>
> Write your report.

2 **KEY PHRASES** Put the phrases in the correct groups. Which are in the article?

It is recommended that ...   It was reported that ...
It was thought that ...   On balance, ...
Taking all the points into consideration, ...
This report is intended to ...

Introduction
The aim of this report is to ...
The report is based on / draws on ...
1 _____

Reporting views
It would seem that ...
According to ...
(People) were of the opinion that ...
2 _____
3 _____

Summing up / Giving your opinion
In conclusion, ...   To conclude, ...   To sum up, ...
4 _____
5 _____

Recommending / Suggesting
I would suggest ...
In my opinion, it would be worth ...
6 _____

Writing Guide

> **Writing Strategy**
> When writing a report:
> - think carefully about the target reader and write in an appropriate style and tone.
> - state the purpose of the report in the first paragraph and any recommendations and suggestions in the final paragraph.
> - consider using headings where appropriate to give the report a clear structure.

Introduction

The aim of this report is to assess the measures taken by the council and to put forward recommendations for further action.

Benefits of the measures taken

According to most residents, the new pedestrian zone is a great success. It was also thought that the bike lanes improved road safety. The coach park on the outskirts of the town has also met with approval, as coaches no longer drive into the centre where the streets are very narrow.

Disadvantages of the measures

The increase in parking charges has discouraged people from driving into town, but local shops and businesses are suffering because fewer people come into town to shop. What is more, it would seem that these charges adversely affect disabled people and elderly people who rely on their cars.

Suggestions for future improvements

The majority of residents are of the opinion that there are not enough open green spaces. In my opinion, it would therefore be worth creating a new park on the wasteland near the station. I would suggest that more free parking places for disabled and elderly people are created. In conclusion, the council has made a good start, but a lot more could be done.

3 Read the Writing Strategy and the task below. Make notes under the headings.

> Last year, your school took measures to make it cleaner and greener. The head teacher would like to hear your views on the measures they have taken and also any suggestions for future improvements.

Your opinion of measures taken
1 _____
  _____
2 _____
  _____
3 _____
  _____

Suggestions for further improvements
1 _____
  _____
2 _____
  _____

4 Write your report.

> **CHECK YOUR WORK**
> **Have you ...**
> ☐ divided the report into paragraphs?
> ☐ used headings?
> ☐ checked your spelling and grammar?

Vocabulary

1 Complete the text with suitable verbs about protesting.

Human rights organisations joined together last weekend to hold a
¹r_____ in support of refugees. The demonstration
also gave people the chance to ²p_____ against the
government's lack of action in the current migrant crisis. People
made placards to ³h_____ up during the march and were
encouraged to ⁴s_____ slogans, such as: 'Say it proud.
Say it clear. Refugees are welcome here.' A meeting was held at
the end of the march where participants could ⁵l_____ to
speeches by leading activists. The total number of protesters is still
unconfirmed, but around 90,000 people said on Facebook that
they ⁶w_____ on the march.

Mark: ____ / 6

2 Complete the sentences with the words below.

censorship   corruption   disease   famine
globalisation   homelessness

1 Ebola is a very contagious _____ which can spread
rapidly from one place to another.

2 _____ is the best thing that has ever happened to
large multinational companies.

3 The government has recently been involved in a number of
scandals involving fraud and _____ .

4 One of the most common approaches to _____ is
to try to put those affected into shelters.

5 A lack of rain has caused a drought, which will in turn lead
to widespread _____ in the area.

6 Social networking sites are often prohibited in countries
where there is _____ of the media.

Mark: ____ / 6

**3 Match the verbs in A with the words in B to make protest
collocations. Then complete the sentences.**

A campaign   sign   stand   support   vote   write

B a campaign   against nuclear power   a petition
in elections   outside the building   to the council

1 Are you allowed to _____ _____ yet, or do
you have to wait until your next birthday?

2 When my friends and I _____ _____ , we
tend to get very involved in it.

3 Why don't you _____ _____ if you don't
agree that the local library should be closed?

4 The protesters are going to _____ _____
until the director comes out to speak to them.

5 Ecology groups often _____ _____ ,
because they say it harms the environment.

6 This morning, I was asked to _____ _____
against the proposed new school timetable.

Mark: ____ / 6

Word Skills

**4 Complete the second sentence so that it means the same
as the first.**

1 It would be better if the speakers had microphones.
I'd prefer _____ .

2 They're printing the flyers this afternoon.
We're getting _____ .

3 That article made me think about changing my diet.
That article had _____ .

4 A professional photographer took the photos.
They had a professional photographer _____
_____ .

5 The teacher made us re-sit the exam.
We were made _____ .

6 My parents refused to go to the rally.
I couldn't get _____ .

Mark: ____ / 6

5 Choose the correct answers (a–c).

1 How many hours of revision did you ___ for your last exam?
a put in   b set up   c think up

2 I'm trying not to ___ too many extracurricular activities this
year.
a help out   b step down   c take on

3 The cyclist managed to ___ of the rest and went on to win
the race.
a set up   b get ahead   c squeeze in

4 Who's going to be the next president of the debating
society when Grace ___ ?
a steps down   b takes on   c helps out

5 She always ___ really crazy inventions.
a puts in   b helps out   c thinks up

6 The organisers have asked me to ___ at the next fundraising
event.
a take on   b get ahead   c help out

Mark: ____ / 6

6 Match the sentence halves.

1 To my mind, ☐
2 It's clear to me that we should ☐
3 I feel quite strongly that shops ☐
4 People might say that recycling's a waste of time, ☐
5 While it's true that fossil fuels are running out, ☐

a but I believe it's better than nothing.
b should charge for plastic bags.
c sugary drinks should be banned.
d I don't think that nuclear power is the solution.
e prioritise the use of oil in the future.

Mark: ____ / 5

Grammar

7 Complete the second and third conditional sentences with the correct form of the verbs in brackets.

1 You _____ money on your electricity bill if you didn't leave the lights on. (save)

2 If I _____ the train, I wouldn't have been late for my job interview. (not miss)

3 You _____ the exam if you'd bothered to study. (not fail)

4 If we _____ to the head teacher, do you think it would make a difference? (speak)

5 I _____ you some money if you'd asked me. (lend)

6 If we _____ a car, I'd have to walk everywhere. (not have)

Mark: ____ / 6

8 Choose the correct words to complete the sentences.

1 I wouldn't have known about the party **even if / supposing / unless** you'd told me. Shall we go together?

2 **Even if / Supposing / Unless** you lost your job, what would you do then? Would you look for another one?

3 I would have enjoyed the concert **even if / supposing / unless** it had rained. I love that band!

4 I wouldn't complain **even if / supposing / unless** there was a problem – and there is!

5 **Even if / Supposing / Unless** we left now, we wouldn't get to the match on time.

Mark: ____ / 5

9 Complete the second sentence so that it means the same as the first.

1 Heidi speaks German because she went to a German school.
If Heidi hadn't gone to a German school, _____
_____ .

2 I haven't got my own room because my parents didn't buy a big house.
If my parents had bought a big house, _____
_____ .

3 He didn't apologise, so I'm angry.
I wouldn't be angry if _____
_____ .

4 I didn't pay for our coffees because I haven't got any money with me.
If I had some money with me, _____
_____ .

Mark: ____ / 4

Use of English

10 Complete the text with the correct form of the words in brackets.

One of the greatest [1]_____ (demonstrate) in history was the 1930 Salt March in India. At the time, there was no [2]_____ (democracy) rule in the country as it was governed by the British. Most government policies were [3]_____ (race) because they favoured British citizens over Indians. Civil rights activist Mahatma Gandhi was the leader in the campaign against this [4]_____ (equal) and he chose Britain's Salt Acts as a symbol for the [5]_____ (just) of the system. These laws prohibited Indians from collecting or selling salt and forced them to buy it from the British. Gandhi's first act was the [6]_____ (organise) of a peaceful march from his hometown to the coast where he would collect salt. On 12 March, he set off with less than a hundred [7]_____ (protest). Along the way, people listened to his [8]_____ (speak) at the meetings he held. Many of them [9]_____ (sympathise) with the cause, and by the time he reached the coast on 5 April, the crowd had swollen to tens of thousands. Although 60,000 arrests were made – including Gandhi himself – the march was [10]_____ (success) in raising awareness of the Civil Disobedience Movement. India was finally granted independence in August 1947.

Mark: ____ / 10

Total: ____ / 60

I can ...

Read the statements. Think about your progress and tick one of the boxes.

★ = I need more practice.   ★★★ = No problem!
★★ = I sometimes find this difficult.

	★	★★	★★★
I can talk about local and global issues.			
I can use second and third conditionals.			
I can use discourse markers to help predict what will be said next.			
I can use mixed conditionals.			
I am aware of and can use different verb patterns.			
I can understand an extract from an American novel.			
I can discuss a question with a partner and work towards an agreement.			
I can write a report about a local issue.			

Exam Skills Trainer

Reading

Strategy

When you do a gapped-sentences task, look at the connecting words in options A–E for clues about what must go before or after them.

1 Read the Strategy and look at sentences A–E in exercise 2. Find and underline the connecting words. What do they indicate: result, reason, purpose, or contrast?

2 Read the text where four sentences are missing. Match the missing sentences (A–E) with the gaps (1–4). There is one extra sentence.

Boston Tea Party

On the cold winter night of 16 December 1773, a group of American colonists approached three British ships anchored in Boston harbour. ¹_____ Once they had boarded the vessels and located the tea that the ships were carrying, they proceeded to empty all 342 of the chests into the sea, destroying their contents forever. At the time, they may not have been aware of the far-reaching implications their actions would have.

The protest, which came to be known as the Boston Tea Party, had its roots in the growing friction between the North American colonists and the British Parliament over the question of taxation. According to the colonists, the British had no right to make them pay taxes as the colonists were not represented in parliament. ²_____ Things came to a head on 10 May 1773 when the Tea Act was passed, which required colonists to purchase only British tea. Although cheaper than other teas, this tea was taxed, a fact that the colonists refused to tolerate.

In New York, Philadelphia and Charleston, the colonists had managed to persuade the authorities to reject the tea shipments that had arrived, forcing the ships to return to Britain. ³_____ It was the tea that was the cause of their complaint, not the ships, so it was the tea that the colonists destroyed. After three hours, 45 tons of it had been dumped into the harbour, a quantity that would be worth around a million dollars today. Not surprisingly, the British were furious.

In response to the action, Parliament passed a set of laws known as the Coercive Acts in an attempt to assert more control over the Boston settlement. The measure had the opposite effect, however, and only succeeded in provoking the other colonies in the area. ⁴_____ This eventually culminated in the American War of Independence (1775–1783), which led to the creation of the nation we now know as the United States of America. It was the Boston Tea Party that set the wheels of independence in motion.

A However, the governor in Boston refused to cooperate, so the colonists took matters into their own hands.

B So as not to reveal their identity, some of them were disguised as Native Americans.

C Owing to the popularity of tea in Europe, rival companies had been set up to import tea from China.

D As a result, all thirteen of them met at the 1774 First Continental Congress to discuss their collaborative resistance to the British.

E Although the colonists had been protesting against this for some time, their voices had fallen on deaf ears.

Listening

Strategy

Before you do a true or false task, look at the statements and underline the key words. Predict three words that you expect to hear in the recording.

3 Read the Strategy and look at the statement below. Underline the key words and choose the group of words you would expect to hear in the recording. What situations do the other groups refer to?

The speakers are at a rally.

A musicians, singer, stage

B crowd, pitch, players

C microphone, placard, speech

4 🎧 2.20 You will hear three texts twice. Are the statements true (T) or false (F)?

Text 1

1 The speakers are teachers. ___

2 They are both in favour of the new reform. ___

Text 2

3 The speaker describes a natural disaster that was nearly as bad as the last one the country suffered. ___

4 The speaker's intention is to appeal for money to help the victims of the disaster. ___

Text 3

5 It is a fact that other European countries have offered more help to refugees than the UK. ___

6 The speaker thinks that British people need to be convinced to welcome more refugees into the country. ___

Use of English

Strategy

A banked cloze task often tests your knowledge of collocations. Always record common collocations with an example sentence in your vocabulary notebook to help you remember which words go together.

5 Read the Strategy. Then match verbs 1–5 with nouns a–e that they collocate with.

1	tell	a	an image
2	make	b	the truth
3	photoshop	c	evidence
4	fabricate	d	a difficulty
5	exaggerate	e	an excuse

6 Complete the text with the words below. There are two extra words.

accused   admitted   disguised   misled   petitions
rallies   revealed   rights   slogans   speeches

Few political protests in the UK have been more dramatic than the fight for women's voting ¹_____ . At the start of the movement, ²_____ were made and ³_____ were signed, all to no avail. In reaction to the lack of response, the campaigners held ⁴_____ and shouted ⁵_____ , but still their voices were not heard – that is, until 4 June 1913, when activist Emily Davison reportedly threw herself in front of the King's horse during an important race at Epsom. Those in favour of granting women the vote praised Davison for her bravery, whereas opponents ⁶_____ her of being irresponsible. Recently, however, a new study of the images taken by news cameras at the scene has ⁷_____ the truth about Davison's fatal intervention. Reports at the time ⁸_____ everyone into thinking that Davison was trying to bring down the King's horse, when in fact she was trying to attach a scarf to it. Further evidence supporting this theory is the fact that two more scarves were found on her body after her death, along with a return train ticket home.

Speaking

Strategy

A situational role-play tests your ability to negotiate with a partner in order to reach an agreement. There will be times when you don't agree with your partner, in which case, you need to disagree tactfully, e.g. *I'm not sure about that.*

7 Read the Strategy. Complete the useful phrases below for disagreeing tactfully with someone.

1 I don't think that's such a good _____ .
2 I'm not convinced that will _____ .
3 That might not be the right _____ to go about it.
4 I don't _____ if that's what we need here.

8 Work in pairs. You and a friend have been asked to design a poster to publicise an environmental campaign among teenagers. Discuss and agree on the following points to decide what the poster should look like.

- topic
- image
- slogan

9 Summarise what you have agreed for each point in exercise 8.

Writing

Strategy

In an opinion essay, you need to use linking expressions to connect and extend your ideas. Not all linking expressions are used in the same position in a sentence.

10 Read the Strategy. Choose the correct answers.

1 Participating in a campaign can be rewarding. **Besides / Too**, you can make new friends.
2 Petitions are a useful means of gathering support for a cause. Demonstrations can attract many followers **also / as well**.
3 Social media posts can sometimes attract unwelcome responses. Our posts can be shared on other people's timelines **in addition / too**.
4 Selecting the appropriate security settings is important. **Furthermore / As well**, it is advisable to check who might be able to view and to share our posts.

11 Read the task below and write your essay.

Some people use their social media accounts to express and publicise their political views. Is this a good idea? Write an essay in which you express your opinion, taking into consideration what effect it may have on the people writing the posts and people responding to them.

9 Consumerism

Vocabulary

A Shopping
I can talk about the consumer society.

1 Complete the text with the correct form of the verbs below.

budget   get into debt   knock down   overcharge
shop around   snap up

I have to buy lots of things at the beginning of the university year. I ¹_____ carefully for everything I need to buy and the most expensive things are my books. So, I always ²_____ and see which shops are selling things the cheapest as I don't want to ³_____ before the year has even started. Fortunately, I saw a 10% discount on books at a local bookshop and decided quickly to ⁴_____ the ones that I needed. However, the shop almost ⁵_____ me! They had forgotten to ⁶_____ the price of the books by 10% on their computers.

2 🎧 **2.21 Listen to five dialogues about money. Match sentences A–F with speakers 1–5. There is one extra sentence.**

This speaker …

A has been spending too much money and has got into debt. ☐

B hasn't picked up any bargains. ☐

C explained that she was almost overcharged for something. ☐

D has been haggling at a local market. ☐

E has splashed out on something that cost a lot. ☐

F has been budgeting for a future activity that will cost a lot of money. ☐

3 🎧 **2.21 Listen again and complete the sentences with the correct form of the verbs below.**

afford   knock down   overspend   shop around   snap up

1 Speaker 1 has been _____ all day.

2 Speaker 2 thinks she will be able to _____ everything on her trip if she saves money.

3 Speaker 3 was able to _____ the price of her laptop by 10%.

4 Speaker 4 has _____ and had to borrow money from a friend.

5 Speaker 5 says she _____ some shoes in the sale.

4 Complete the sentences with one word in each gap.

1 If you overspend, you might get into _____ .

2 If you _____ at the market, the stall owner might knock _____ the price.

3 If you _____ around, you might find things cheaper.

4 If you shop in the sales, you might _____ up some bargains.

5 If you _____ for how much you can spend before you go shopping, you won't spend more money than you can _____ .

6 It's always a good idea to check the receipt after you buy something to make sure you haven't been _____ .

5 Replace the underlined phrases with the words below.

delivery   items   notification   reviews   track   wish list

I've been waiting for a number of ¹goods that I ordered online. I had a ²list of things that I wanted and decided to buy everything on it! I've been to the website to ³follow the progress of my order, but there's no information. Neither have I received a ⁴message with information about ⁵when they will brings the goods to my house. The ⁶customer opinions of this site were positive, but my experience of it isn't!

6 Complete the definitions.

1 A w_____ l_____ is a list of things that you want to buy.

2 A c_____ o_____ is a place where you pay for goods.

3 A n_____ is information sent to someone about something.

4 An i_____ is an individual unit, often part of a list or group.

5 A b_____ is a place on a website where you can see the goods you have decided to buy. It is also a physical thing that you use in a supermarket.

6 A r_____ is an opinion about a product or service.

7 A d_____ involves goods, letters, parcels, etc. being taken to a person's house, office, or place of work.

8 When you t_____ something, you follow it by using a website or electronic equipment.

Emphasis

I can use sentence structure to create emphasis.

1 Complete the second sentence so that it means the same as the first.

1 Chris lost his phone yesterday.
It was Chris _____ .

2 Ella is getting her hair cut tomorrow.
It's tomorrow _____ .

3 His grandparents moved to New Zealand last year.
It's New Zealand _____ .

4 My brother wasn't born until 2010.
It wasn't until _____ .

5 Nick has been learning to ride a motorbike.
It's a _____ .

6 I have guitar lessons on Saturday mornings.
It's on _____ .

7 We saw Roberto at the club last night.
It was Roberto _____ .

8 They don't enjoy watching sci-fi films.
It's sci-fi films _____ .

2 Rewrite the sentences to make a contrast. Begin with the words given and emphasise the words in bold.

1 This bag is made of **leather**. It's not made of plastic.
It's leather that _____ .

2 The film doesn't finish at 8 p.m. It finishes at **9 p.m.**
It's at _____ .

3 My sister didn't give me this present. **Leo** did.
It was _____ .

4 I prefer the **blue** dress. I don't prefer the grey one.
It's the _____ .

5 Tom doesn't drive a Ferrari. He drives a **Porsche.**
It's a _____ .

6 Sam isn't going on holiday to Turkey. **Dan** is.
It's Dan _____ .

7 School finishes in **June**. It doesn't finish in July.
It's in _____ .

3 Rewrite the sentences beginning with *What* or *All.*

1 This chicken needs to be cooked a bit longer.
What _____ .

2 You only need to answer two of the exam questions.
All _____ .

3 Jenny returned the broken watch to the shop.
What _____ .

4 We'll just have to buy some drinks for the barbecue.
All _____ .

5 No one can remember the name of the new café.
What _____ .

6 The only thing I know about our new neighbours is that they are Swedish.
All _____ .

7 You mustn't forget to turn off the TV before bedtime.
What _____ .

4 Write the words in the correct order to make emphatic sentences.

1 who / Eva / that / The / person / dog / owns / is
_____

2 I / is / thing / spiders / can't / One / stand
_____

3 often / is / A / to / they've / place / Japan / been
_____

4 who / most / Adele / singer / she / is / The / loves
_____

5 doesn't / green / colour / like / The / Laila / is
_____

6 try / octopus / food / never / One / I'll / is / !
_____

7 like / snowboarding / try / A / he'd / is / sport / to
_____

5 Choose the correct words to complete the forum post.

> ◀ ▶ [   ] ↻
>
> Why do teenagers always get the blame for everything?
> [1]**One / What** thing that really annoys me is getting
> blamed for all the litter in town, when [2]**it was / it's**
> often the adults who don't use the bins. [3]**Where / What**
> the authorities need to do is put CCTV cameras outside
> so they can see who's responsible! But [4]**a / the** main
> problem they need to address is providing somewhere
> for us to go. One [5]**place / thing** where we can hang
> out is at fast-food restaurants, so [6]**it's / what's** there
> that people see us in groups and assume we're causing
> trouble. [7]**All / One** we want is somewhere we can go
> and enjoy ourselves! **dexy33**

6 Complete the text with one word in each gap.

We know that plastic is to blame for much of the world's pollution, but [1]_____ was the news that a plastic island the size of Texas is forming in the Pacific Ocean that shocked many of us. [2]_____ answer that many countries have come up with is charging customers for plastic bags in shops. And [3]_____ some countries have done is to completely ban bags that aren't biodegradable. Since these laws were introduced, the use of plastic bags globally has dropped dramatically. [4]_____ thing you can do to help is to buy a 'bag for life' from a supermarket. When it wears out, [5]_____ you need to do is take it back to get a free replacement. In some countries, the [6]_____ place where you still won't be charged for a plastic bag is at an airport or on planes.

SOME PEOPLE ARE SO POOR, ALL THEY HAVE IS MONEY

1 Read the text and decide whether sentences 1–4 are fact (F) or opinion (O).

1 ☐ 2 ☐ 3 ☐ 4 ☐

Rich without money

Living without money is not easy. You have to really want to do it and be prepared to give up some things. You will need to lose the impulse to just buy anything you want. ¹However, you will find another way of living in which you will be happy with all that you already have. And it will be a more creative life that you develop to satisfy your needs. ²You will be rich in other ways! In addition, you won't be contributing to the destruction of the environment caused by all the stuff we buy that we don't need.

But imagine what a whole world would be like without money. Would it even be possible? ³In fact, philosophers, sociologists and economists have already asked these questions. When money was introduced into our society, it made our lives so much easier in many ways. So would it be impossible to go back now?

Well, there is a middle way. ⁴There are many websites which give people tips on relying less on money, and practical advice on other ways of doing things.

Why not have a look and try some of the ideas? You can save not only money, but also the environment. What have you got to lose?

> **Listening Strategy**
> To answer some comprehension questions, you need to be able to distinguish between fact and opinion. Listen carefully for words or phrases that may indicate whether the speaker is expressing a fact or an opinion.

2 Read the Listening Strategy. Then put the phrases below in the correct columns.

actually   as far as I'm concerned   as I see it
in fact   in my view   in reality   I strongly believe
I've a feeling that   it's been proved that   it's true that
it's undeniable that   my impression is   personally
the truth is   to my mind   undeniably

Introducing an opinion	Introducing a fact

3 🎧 2.22 Listen and write the words used to introduce the sentences. Are the sentences fact (F) or opinion (O)?

1 _____ , bank managers get paid too much. ☐

2 _____ inflation has remained at the same level for six months. ☐

3 _____ , the government's policies to tackle poverty aren't working. ☐

4 _____ it's better to be a saver than a spender. ☐

5 _____ more Monopoly money is printed every year than real money. ☐

6 _____ the key to happiness is spending money on experiences rather than possessions. ☐

4 🎧 2.23 Listen to three recordings and choose the correct answers (a–c).

1 What is the purpose of the speaker's story?
   a To show how money changes relationships.
   b To explain why it is better to be poor.
   c To persuade people to live without money.

2 The speakers can't agree that
   a people are generally nice.
   b couch-surfing has a good philosophy behind it.
   c couch-surfing doesn't cost anything.

3 Which of the following is stated in the radio programme as an opinion, not a fact?
   a Streetbank is an online project.
   b The co-founders of Streetbank intended to encourage community spirit.
   c There is no negative side to Streetbank.

9D

Participle clauses

I can use participle clauses.

1 Choose the correct words to complete the sentences.

1 **Taking** / **Taken** with a glass of water, these tablets will cure a headache.
2 That lady **talking** / **talked** on the phone must be the manager.
3 **Having slept** / **Sleeping** badly last night, Jaime is in a bad mood.
4 **Worn** / **Wearing** with a red shirt, these black trousers would look fabulous.
5 **Discovered** / **Having discovered** last year, the temple is thought to be thousands of years old.
6 Suddenly **realised** / **realising** how late it was, we decided to go home.
7 **Being** / **Been** a fan of Sherlock Holmes, I have all the Conan Doyle novels.

2 Choose the correct options (a–c) to complete the text.

The most popular time for people to go shopping used to be during the January sales. Now, in some parts of the world there is one particular day that sees shoppers go wild! ¹__ 'Black Friday', it takes place in November. ²__ Thanksgiving, one of the USA's biggest holidays, on the following Friday millions of Americans rush to the shops, ³__ to save money on their Christmas shopping. Although still ⁴__ mainly in the USA, Black Friday has also spread to shops in Canada, Mexico and the UK. And ⁵__ to miss out on making money, online stores are also joining in, ⁶__ huge bargains to their customers. ⁷__ sensibly, it's a great opportunity for shoppers, but it has also been criticised by many for encouraging consumerism.

1 **a** Calling	**b** Called	**c** Having called
2 **a** Celebrating	**b** Celebrated	**c** Having celebrated
3 **a** hoping	**b** having hoped	**c** hoped
4 **a** taken place	**b** taking place	**c** having taken place
5 **a** not wanting	**b** not having wanted	**c** not wanted
6 **a** offered	**b** having offered	**c** offering
7 **a** Approached	**b** Approaching	**c** Having approached

3 Write the words in the correct order to make sentences with participle clauses. Insert a comma in the correct place.

1 this / taste / Cooked / will / delicious / slowly / meat

_____

2 the / exam / celebrating / passed / are / Having / their / students

_____

3 to / Feeling / lie-in / I've / have / a / lazy / decided

_____

4 he / the / on / climbed / ladder / Holding / up / tight

_____

5 blowing / the / There / breeze / a / trees / was / through

_____

6 very / year / is / Born / nephew / cute / last / my

_____

4 Complete the sentences with the words below.

After finishing	Before leaving	On checking
Since starting	When thinking	While playing

1 _____ the house, could you do the washing up?
2 _____ at her new school, my sister's made lots of new friends.
3 _____ breakfast, they went out for a walk.
4 _____ tennis, Petra fell and hurt her ankle.
5 _____ his change, he realised the shop assistant had made a mistake.
6 _____ about where to go on holiday, you should consider the price as well as the location.

5 Complete the letter with one word in each gap.

Dear Sir

I am writing about some boots I recently purchased from your online store. ¹H_____ looked at all the designs available, I chose a pair of brown biker boots. The boots I received do not look like the photo on your website. ²M_____ of leather, these boots should be very comfortable, but ³o_____ wearing them, I found them to be quite tight and painful. ⁴B_____ a student, I have very little money, and ⁵s_____ receiving the boots, I've found a similar pair much cheaper elsewhere. I'm sure you must have other customers ⁶g_____ you similar feedback, and I hope you will give me a full refund if I return the boots to you.

Yours

N Kowalski

Money idioms

I can use money idioms.

1 Complete the sentences with the correct words.

1 How much did you pay for that jacket? What a _____-off!

2 If I weren't so _____ , I could afford to come out tonight.

3 Vic used to be _____ off before his business failed and he lost everything.

4 Do you think it's possible to be _____ up, but still be very happy?

5 You can often buy fruit and vegetables dirt _____ at the weekly market.

6 My family aren't exactly _____ in it, but we live quite comfortably.

2 Match the sentence halves.

1 I'll have to tighten my ☐

2 You'll never make ends ☐

3 After living hand to ☐

4 Very few people make ☐

5 Ben's careful with money so he's never been in ☐

6 We had to pay ☐

7 I often dream about living in ☐

a the red for very long.

b mouth for years, she finally became a successful writer.

c a fortune through playing the lottery.

d belt next month or I'll soon run out of money.

e the lap of luxury, but it's unlikely to happen.

f meet if you spend more than you earn.

g through the nose for the concert tickets, but it was worth it!

3 Tick the pairs of idioms that have a similar meaning.

1 live hand to mouth / be well off ☐

2 be rolling in it / live in the lap of luxury ☐

3 be hard up / be a rip-off ☐

4 make a killing / make a fortune ☐

5 be broke / be in the red ☐

6 make ends meet / pay through the nose ☐

7 be dirt cheap / tighten one's belt ☐

4 Complete the text with idioms from exercise 3.

Many common idioms have interesting origins which can help to explain their meanings. For instance, [1]_____ apparently replaced the former 'be dog cheap' to indicate something of very little value. [2]_____ comes from the accounting practice of using that colour ink for debts and black for credit. [3]_____ may also come from accounting, when the 'ends' or bottoms of the columns for the incomes and expenses were the same amount, or 'met', showing that more wasn't being spent than was earned. [4]_____ comes from prison slang, in which 'rip' means 'steal', so someone who does this to others is a thief. [5]_____ apparently dates back to a 16th century famine when people were so poor that any food they got was eaten immediately so that no one else could have it. [6]_____ is thought to date from the Great Depression of the 1930s, when hungry Americans lost so much weight that their clothes became loose.

> **VOCAB BOOST!**
>
> Try to find out the literal meaning of idioms to help make them more memorable. Often, although not always, this meaning has a logical or metaphonical connection to the meaning of the idiom.

5 Read the *Vocab boost!* box. Then match the idioms and their literal meanings (1–4) with their actual meanings (a–d).

1 **to be born with a silver spoon in your mouth** ☐
Spoons are often given to babies as presents. Silver used to be an expensive metal and it's probable that richer children were given silver spoons.

2 **a cash cow** ☐
This is a metaphor for a dairy cow, which produces milk.

3 **to live on the breadline** ☐
In America during the Depression, people would wait in line to be given free food, paid for by the government.

4 **money for old rope** ☐
The original meaning for this term meant to make money by selling something that has been used and ought to be worthless. It comes from the days of sailing ships, when sailors would cut damaged rope into shorter, undamaged lengths to sell on land. At sea, long ropes are needed, but on land, shorter lengths were still useful and could be sold.

a to be very poor

b to make money for very little effort

c to be privileged

d business or invention that returns a good level of profit every year

6 Check the meaning of these idioms in a dictionary.

1 feel the pinch

2 cost the earth

3 work for peanuts

4 cost an arm and a leg

5 keep your head above water

6 put your money where your mouth is

The history of the shopping mall

I can understand a text about the design of shopping malls.

Revision: Student's Book page 102

1 Match the words below with the definitions.

brand   commercial   consumer   endorsement
jingle   launch   logo   slogan

1 A short song or slogan that is used in TV and radio adverts. _____

2 A symbol used by a company to identify its products. _____

3 The act of saying that you support or approve of somebody or something. _____

4 A type of product made by a company with a particular name. _____

5 An event to introduce something new. _____

6 A short phrase that is easy to remember, often used to advertise a product. _____

7 An advertisement that is broadcast on TV or radio. _____

8 A person who buys goods or services. _____

2 Read the text. Find three ways in which shopping malls try to encourage people to spend their money.

Reading Strategy

Read the missing sentences carefully before you match them with the gaps in the text. Look at the parts of the text before and after each gap, and try to find words that may link them to the sentences, for example synonyms, paraphrases, opposites or pronouns.

3 Read the Reading Strategy. Then read the text again. Match sentences A–F with gaps 1–4 in the text. There are two extra sentences.

A This took away a major obstacle between shoppers and the brands on sale inside.

B Despite that, if you spend a little time looking around the next mall you visit, you'll see that Taubman's ideas are still being put into practice.

C However, seldom do shoppers notice that the day seems to last longer in a shopping mall.

D The layout of a modern shopping mall is very similar to the layout of those first malls from nearly seventy years ago.

E Restaurants and cafés were placed at the end of the malls because they were only used at certain times of the day.

F The idea was to create a space that people would feel like spending a whole day in.

THE *kings* OF THE SHOPPING MALL

It was on 22 March 1954 that the world's first shopping mall, Northland, opened. Built in a suburb of Chicago, USA, the designer of Northland, Victor Gruen, told the press that it was the 'shopping centre of the future'. Gruen was half-right, because although Northland was the world's first purpose-built shopping centre, it was his next design, Southdale in Minnesota, that became the model that architects all over the world would copy. Opened two years after Northland, Southdale was the first shopping centre where the shops were enclosed in one enormous building, and shopping mall architects have followed Gruen's model ever since. [1]___

However, if Victor Gruen invented the mall, businessman Alfred Taubman perfected it. Taubman took Gruen's design and added a few rules to encourage consumers to spend as much money as possible. Taubman decided that shops should only occupy two floors. Furthermore, the escalators to move shoppers between the floors should always be at the two ends of the mall, forcing people to walk past all the shops on a floor. He also insisted on glass safety barriers on the first floor, allowing consumers to easily see the shops above and below them, and on opening up the front of shops completely by removing their big glass windows. [2]___ Taubman also wanted shoppers to spend as much time as possible in the malls so they would spend more money. He suggested letting plenty of natural light into them by constructing huge glass ceilings. Taubman also installed artificial lights next to the glass ceilings, so that as daylight faded, the artificial light increased and shoppers were unaware of the passing of time. Holding different events every week and local festivals in the space inside the mall would bring in even more people. [3]___

Today, shopping malls have grown to the size of small towns and contain a lot of leisure facilities such as theme parks, artificial lakes and even ski slopes to attract customers. [4]___ However, although shopping malls are carefully designed to make consumers part with as much of their money as possible, it is unlikely that they will notice. Many people see a visit to a shopping mall as a leisure activity and that is perhaps Taubman's biggest legacy.

Photo comparison
I can compare photos.

1 🎧 2.24 Read the task below. Then listen to a student doing the task. Which option does he choose and why?

> Compare the photos. Say which of these places is more suitable for a birthday treat for a friend.

2 🎧 2.24 Listen again. Tick the phrases below that the student uses for justifying his opinion.

1 The reason I believe that is because ... ☐
2 The main reason is that ... ☐
3 For one thing, ... / Another thing is that ... ☐
4 On top of that, ... ☐
5 I definitely think that the ... is better, because ... ☐
6 For those reasons, I think ... ☐

> **Speaking Strategy**
>
> When performing the task, it is important that you have useful language ready at your disposal. For example:
>
> **Introducing opinions** In my view, ...
>
> **Making additional points** Not only that, but ...
>
> **Giving examples** for instance
>
> **Introducing contrasting points** However, ...
>
> **Gaining time** That's an interesting question.

3 🎧 2.24 KEY PHRASES Read the Speaking Strategy and listen again. Add the formulaic phrases that you hear to the correct groups below.

Introducing opinions
To my mind, ...
1 _____

Making additional points
Not only that, but ...
In addition to that, ...

Giving examples
2 _____

Introducing contrasting points
3 _____
However, ...
4 _____

Gaining time
That's an interesting question.
5 _____

4 Match 1–5 with a–e to make phrases to express a tentative opinion.

1 I don't have any strong ___
2 I'm not sure about ___
3 It could be ___
4 There might be a case ___
5 Thinking about it, I ___

a that. Let me think / see.
b argued that ...
c opinion about ...
d suppose that ...
e for arguing that ...

5 🎧 2.25 Listen to another student answering the examiner's follow-up question. Which of the phrases in exercise 4 does she use?

> Compare the photos. Which place would you choose for a day out with a penfriend who is visiting the UK from another country?

6 Read the task above. Spend about a minute preparing your answer.

Your preferred option
_____

Reasons
_____
_____

> Which place would you prefer to live in?

7 Read the follow-up question above and write notes. Try not to spend long on preparing your answer.
_____
_____

8 Now do the task using your notes from exercises 6 and 7.

9H Writing
A letter to a newspaper
I can write a letter about solutions to a problem.

Preparation

A newspaper published an article saying that teenagers with part-time jobs spend the extra money wastefully and also get lower school grades due to their jobs. Write a letter to the editor where you express your opinion and suggest ways that part-time work could be beneficial to teenagers.

1 Read the task above and the letter opposite. Answer the questions below. Do you agree with the student's reaction?

   1 What is the student's reaction to the article?
   2 What positive reasons are given for part-time jobs?
   3 How many suggestions are made for making part-time work beneficial?

> **Writing Strategy**
> Use synonyms and paraphrases to avoid repeating the same words too often, for example: *very angry = furious*.

2 Read the Writing Strategy. Then read the words and phrases below and match them with the highlighted words with similar meanings in the letter.

   1 arrive _____
   2 belief/view _____
   3 cut back _____
   4 claimed that _____
   5 presenting _____
   6 keep _____
   7 refused _____
   8 put forward _____
   9 function _____
   10 in answer to _____
   11 giving _____
   12 urgent _____

Writing Guide

A newspaper recently published an article about teenagers spending all their money on unnecessary consumer goods, blaming their obsession with the latest technology. Write a letter to the editor where you express your opinion about this, and suggest ways that teenagers can be helped to really think about their needs and to buy wisely.

3 Read the task above. Make notes.

Your reaction _____

Your reasons _____

_____

Your suggestions _____

_____

4 Write your letter to the newspapers using your notes from exercise 3.

Dear Sir or Madam

I am writing in response to the article about part-time work for teenagers. It stated that working was having a negative effect on teenagers by providing them with too much money and reducing the amount of time they spent studying.

I'd like to say that I cannot agree with the assumption that all teenagers who work are very materialistic and are failing at school. I feel that the article is projecting an unbalanced view of teenagers who work. Personally, I think that working teenagers gain experience of how to operate in the real world. They learn to turn up on time, be responsible, and deal with people. They also learn the value of money. To my mind, these are great benefits. Furthermore, many teenagers are saving for worthwhile things like hobbies or university, rather than wasting their earnings.

However, I am sure it is true that those who work very long hours have less study time, which cannot be good. So, I would like to suggest some ways that part-time work may benefit teenagers without affecting their studies. Firstly, they need to limit the hours they work and not work on too many school evenings. Secondly, they could look for casual jobs like babysitting or dog walking, which can be turned down if schoolwork is pressing. Finally, teenagers could work in the holidays rather than school time.

I believe that these suggestions would help teenagers retain the benefits of extra money from working, without putting their studies at risk.

Yours faithfully

Sophie Bennett

> **CHECK YOUR WORK**
> **Have you ...**
> ☐ covered both elements of the task in your letter?
> ☐ started and finished your letter correctly?
> ☐ used synonyms to avoid repetition where possible?

Review Unit 9

Vocabulary

1 Complete the sentences with the verbs below.

afford   knock down   rip off   shop around   snap up
splash out

1 Some restaurants try to _____ their customers by demanding a 20% service charge.
2 I missed the bus but I couldn't _____ a taxi so I had to walk.
3 When I get paid at the end of the summer, I'm going to _____ on a new smartphone.
4 You'll probably save money if you _____ before buying a new laptop.
5 I'm hoping to _____ a bargain in the sales.
6 They'll probably _____ the price of those watches if no one buys them.

Mark: ____ / 6

2 Complete the sentences with words related to online shopping.

1 I created a w_____ l_____ on a site selling computer games. Before my birthday, I gave it to my parents.
2 It's a good idea to look through the details of your order when you get to the c_____ .
3 I'm going to check my b_____ to make sure everything I want to order is in there.
4 The great thing about that company is that you can t_____ the progress of your order.
5 I usually try to order several i_____ at once to save on postage and packing.
6 Most of the online r_____ said the camera wasn't very good, so I decided not to buy it.

Mark: ____ / 6

Word Skills

3 Complete the sentences with money idioms formed from the word in brackets.

1 They'll be _____ until they finish paying for their new house. (hard)
2 Despite the country's supposed wealth, many of the citizens live _____ . (hand)
3 What must it feel like to never have to work and live in _____ ? (lap)
4 I forgot my phone charger so I had to pay _____ for a new one at the airport. (nose)
5 My sister's a single parent, so she finds it hard to _____ . (ends)
6 My bank notifies me if I am _____ so that I can make a deposit before I get charged. (red)

Mark: ____ / 6

4 Complete the definitions with words related to advertising.

1 A l_____ is an image that represents a company.
2 A c_____ is an advert on the radio or the TV.
3 A b_____ is a type of product made by a company.
4 A l_____ is the moment a product is made available to the public for the first time.
5 A s_____ is a memorable phrase often used to draw people's attention to commercial products.
6 A j_____ is a tune that is easy to remember.

Mark: ____ / 6

5 Complete the responses with the phrases below.

Another thing is   For one thing   For those reasons
I definitely think   I don't have any   On top of that
Thinking about it

A Is it better to buy books online or from a bookshop?
B ¹_____ , I suppose that it's better to buy them online.
C ²_____ it's better to buy them from a bookshop. ³_____ , you can read the first page to make sure you like the book. ⁴_____ that you don't have to wait for it to arrive to start reading it. ⁵_____ we need to support bookshops or they might die out. ⁶_____ , I think it's better to buy books from a bookshop than to buy them online.
D ⁷_____ strong opinions about that.

Mark: ____ / 7

Grammar

6 Complete the second sentence with emphasis.

1 I'm just asking for a little more consideration.
   All I'm asking _____
   _____ .
2 I cut my foot on a piece of glass.
   It was a piece of glass _____
   _____
3 Everyone should recycle their waste.
   What everyone should do _____
   _____ .
4 The oil tanker hit a rock.
   What happened _____
   _____
5 You only need to take your rubbish home with you.
   All you need _____
   _____ .

Mark: ____ / 5

7 Complete the second sentence with emphasis.

1 I'd love to visit Hong Kong.
One place _____ Hong Kong.

2 I can't stand queuing in the supermarket.
The thing _____ queuing in the supermarket.

3 You must go to Harrods.
One shop _____ Harrods.

4 I spoke to the manager.
The person _____ the manager.

5 I feel sorry for sales staff who have to work on Sundays.
The people _____ sales staff who have to work on Sundays.

6 I avoid buying any product that is tested on animals.
One thing _____ any product that is tested on animals.

Mark: ___ / 6

8 Choose the correct verb forms to complete the sentences.

1 **Being** / **Been** well off, Sebastian's parents could afford to send him to a private school.

2 **Purchasing** / **Purchased** online, plane tickets are usually cheaper.

3 **Standing** / **Stood** at the checkout, I remembered that I needed to buy bread.

4 **Having got** / **Had got** into debt once, Anne has limited the use of her credit card.

5 The market was full of tourists **haggling** / **haggled** for souvenirs.

6 **Selling** / **Sold** in an attractive gift box, this perfume makes an excellent present.

Mark: ___ / 6

9 Complete the second sentence so that it means the same as the first. Use the words below and the correct participle forms. Write four words in each gap.

although   before   on   since

1 I tried the jeans on and then I bought them.
_____ , I tried them on.

2 I'm getting loads of information about courses now that I've applied for university.
_____ , I'm getting loads of information about courses.

3 The product didn't take off despite the fact that it had been predicted to succeed.
_____ , the product didn't take off.

4 I noticed we hadn't been charged for our drinks when I checked the bill.
_____ , I noticed we hadn't been charged for our drinks.

Mark: ___ / 4

Use of English

10 Complete the sentences with the correct form of the words below.

argue   be   charge   consume   deliver   notify   roll   tight

1 We complained about the bill because we'd been
_____ .

2 My neighbours have just bought a Lamborghini. They must be _____ in it!

3 The company hasn't got a tracking system so they can't send _____ to their customers.

4 There might be a case for _____ against genetically modified food.

5 We had to _____ our belts when my dad lost his job.

6 These days, _____ tend to compare prices more before they decide what to buy.

7 I stayed in all morning waiting for the _____ , but it didn't arrive.

8 _____ dirt cheap, the flip-flops sold out in no time.

Mark: ___ / 8

Total: ___ / 60

I can ...

Read the statements. Think about your progress and tick one of the boxes.

★ = I need more practice.   ★★★ = No problem!

★★ = I sometimes find this difficult.

	★	★★	★★★
I can talk about the consumer society.			
I can use sentence structure to create emphasis.			
I can distinguish between fact and opinion.			
I can use participle clauses.			
I can use money idioms.			
I can understand an article about the design of shopping malls.			
I can compare two photos.			
I can write a letter about solutions to a problem.			

Exam Skills Trainer

Reading

1 Read the Strategy. Then read the text in exercise 2 and the question below. Skim the text and find the bold words from the question. Why is this paragraph not the right answer? What is the right answer?

In which paragraph does the author mention

1 the typical duties performed in this **line of work**?

2 **Read the text. Match paragraphs A–C with questions 1–6. Each paragraph matches two questions.**

In which paragraph does the author mention …

1 an extra received on top of the wages? ___

2 something that might give away the identity of the worker? ___

3 a trend which has changed employment prospects? ___

4 typical consumer behaviour? ___

5 the difficulty of finding a job in the field? ___

6 a good reason for doing the job? ___

A secret job in the retail trade

A I am in a supermarket, doing my best to look like any other shopper browsing the shelves. My mission on this trip is to buy something I fancy from the bakery, which means I'll have to interact with the person at the counter. I'm hoping to pass off the handwritten notes I'm carrying as a shopping list, because no one must know why I am here. I have to keep my identity secret because I am a mystery shopper.

B My job involves visiting five to ten different stores a day and scoring them on, among other things, their appearance and cleanliness. With the €20 I am given to spend at each store, I purchase the obligatory item that enables me to assess the service I receive at the checkout. Adding the value of my purchase to the €225 I make in a typical day of eight hours of visits and two hours filing reports, I earn more than enough to live on.

C However, assignments paying as well as mine are becoming few and far between due to the soaring demand in my line of work. Retailers increasingly need to maintain standards so as to offer consumers a quality shopping experience and keep them from turning to the internet. However, to date, there are more than half a million mystery shoppers registered in the UK, making competition for jobs very fierce. Today it isn't only other shoppers I hide my identity from; even my friends and family don't know who I work for.

Listening

3 Read the Strategy. Then read the short extract below. The question to match with the extract is about taking advantage of somebody else's mistake. Where does this information come: at the beginning, in the middle, or at the end of the extract? Underline the relevant part of the paragraph.

🎧 I picked up a great bargain on eBay the last time I bought a smartphone. I was after a Samsung, and I was bidding for one of the older models because I didn't want to fork out for a new one. One day, I made an important discovery. When I wrote the name of the phone in the search bar, a completely different page came up and the model I wanted was much cheaper. What had happened was that I'd spelled 'Samsung' wrong – without the G – which is what the person who'd listed the phone must have done too.

4 🎧 **2.26** You will hear four speakers talking about bargains they have purchased. Match sentences A–E with speakers 1–4. There is one extra sentence.

Which speaker …

A had a pleasant surprise when they tried something different?

B paid next to nothing for a second-hand object?

C saved a lot of money because of a technological error?

D had to negotiate a price with the seller?

E was given a bargain as a present?

Speaker 1: ___   Speaker 3: ___

Speaker 2: ___   Speaker 4: ___

Use of English

5 Read the Strategy. Then match the groups of words (1–6) with the negative prefixes below.

dis- il- im- in- ir- un-

1 ___ flexible hospitable sensitive
2 ___ rational regular relevant
3 ___ educated noticed skilled
4 ___ coloured content enchanted
5 ___ mature modest probable
6 ___ legal legible literate

6 Complete each gap in the text with a word formed from the word in brackets.

Shopping abroad

In many countries, haggling is more a ¹_____ (CULTURE) tradition than a way of saving money. The problem is that people who aren't used to it tend to feel ²_____ (SECURE) about using the technique. Before starting out, you should have shopped around to give you an idea of prices, so as not to be ³_____ (CHARGE). If you're a beginner, bear in mind that the stall ⁴_____ (HOLD) has far more experience than you, so you should not ⁵_____ (ESTIMATE) his or her skill. On the other hand, there's no point in being ⁶_____ (PUSH), as they are unlikely to offer you a good price if they think you're rude. The most ⁷_____ (EFFECT) strategy is to pretend that you don't care about the item if the seller refuses to lower the price. Just act as though you're not ⁸_____ (INTEREST) and walk away, and the trader will probably come after you.

Speaking

> **Strategy**
> When you compare and contrast photographs, you often have to speculate about what is happening in the pictures.

7 Read the Strategy. Then complete the sentences with the words below.

as like look might perhaps probably

1 She doesn't _____ very happy about the situation.
2 _____ he's been working all day.
3 He looks _____ if he's going to fall off the ladder.
4 They're _____ going to be late.
5 They look _____ store detectives.
6 She _____ be a professional photographer.

8 Compare and contrast the photos which show different methods of payment. Include the following points:
- where you think the customers are shopping
- what you think they have bought
- why you think they are paying in this way

9 In pairs, discuss questions 1 and 2 below. Use evidence from the photos in your discussion, if possible.

1 What are the advantages and disadvantages of using this method of payment?
2 How do you think customers will pay for their shopping in the future?

Writing

> **Strategy**
> When a task requires you to suggest solutions to a problem, do not only list your ideas or suggestions, but explain how each of them can help solve the problem.

10 Match the sentence halves to complete the suggestions.

I would like to suggest some ways of encouraging people to buy eco-friendly products.

1 Firstly, green products should be cheaper. This way ___
2 Secondly, they must be advertised on TV. Not only will it ___
3 Finally, eco-friendly goods ought to be of very high quality. If they were, ___

A their owners and users would recommend them to their friends and neighbours.
B people will buy more of them for less money.
C encourage people to get them, but having and using them will become fashionable.

11 Read the task below and write your letter.

A magazine has recently published an article about the role of money in our lives. Its author claims that the richer we become, the less we care about other people. Write a letter to the editor where you express your opinion, and suggest ways in which people with higher incomes can contribute more to society.

Bank of England

Ten Pounds

"I declare after all there is no enjoyment like r

Listening

1 **🎧 2.27** Listen to four speakers talking about having their photo in a newspaper or a magazine. Match speakers 1–4 with sentences A–E. There is one extra sentence.

A He/She was critical of the person who took the photo. ☐

B He/She was disappointed about the way the photo had turned out. ☐

C He/She was indifferent about having the photo taken. ☐

D He/She was enthusiastic about posing for photos. ☐

E He/She was impressed with the photographer. ☐

Speaking

2 **Work in pairs. Look at the photo below and answer the questions.**

1 How do you think the person is feeling?

2 Do you think parents should always be invited to ceremonies at school?

3 Talk about a school ceremony that you have attended and what happened.

Reading

3 **Read the text on the next page and choose the correct answers.**

1 Since 1970, the Bank of England has been printing banknotes featuring

a kings and queens on the back.

b famous people from the past on the back.

c fictional characters on the back.

d current celebrities on the back.

2 Caroline Criado-Perez and her supporters were protesting because

a they didn't think Winston Churchill should replace Elizabeth Fry.

b they wanted more representatives from English literature on the banknotes.

c they didn't want all of the notes to feature men.

d they thought women should be represented on more than one banknote.

3 Caroline Criado-Perez closed one of her social media accounts because

a she was receiving too many messages.

b she was being harassed by her opponents.

c she was being stalked by one of her supporters.

d she was resigning from the campaign.

4 The new selection process for future banknote characters will be

a more focused on the arts.

b quicker to respond to criticism.

c more representative of women.

d more democratic than before.

5 The portrait of Jane Austen on the new £10 note

a is based on a picture by her sister.

b was painted by a close relative.

c was drawn by her brother.

d is taken from one of the writer's novels.

Finding the right face

You'd think it would be quite straightforward to choose a historical figure to include on a banknote, wouldn't you? Of course, the current monarch needs to be on the front of the note; the problem is who should appear on the back. Back in 1970, when the Bank of England began featuring past celebrities on its £5, £10, £20 and £50 notes, nobody used to question the choices. But that changed in 2013, when it was announced that the £10 note was going to be redesigned.

Just before this announcement, former British Prime Minister Winston Churchill had been chosen to replace prison reformer Elizabeth Fry on the new £5 note. The fact that there were now no women on the back of the banknotes made a woman the logical choice for the £10 note. Feminist activist Caroline Criado-Perez led a campaign to put pressure on the Bank of England to choose the novelist Jane Austen for the note. Criado-Perez and her supporters organised protests, sent out an online petition – signed by 35,000 people – and threatened legal action if their demands were not met.

This was only the start of the trouble, however. On the day the Bank of England announced that the new £10 note would, indeed, feature the author, social media sites were flooded with angry comments. There were attacks on the Bank of England for being too cautious in their choice, attacks on Jane Austen for being old-fashioned and, worse still, personal attacks on Criado-Perez and her supporters for promoting the choice of a woman. When she began to receive death threats, the activist closed her Twitter account.

In response to the incident, the Bank of England announced that it would review the selection process in order to avoid such ugly reactions in future. Since then, a special committee has been set up to deal with the process. From now on, whenever a banknote has to be changed, the committee will choose a particular field, for example the visual arts, and the public will have two months to send in ideas. After that, a shortlist of candidates will be compiled and the governor of the Bank of England will choose a character from the list.

Meanwhile, plans for the Jane Austen banknote are going ahead. The new design features a portrait of the author, adapted from a sketch by her sister, Cassandra. In the centre of the note are the author's writing table and an image of her brother's house, which was the inspiration for a number of novels. There is also an illustration of one of Jane's characters, Elizabeth Bennet, and a quotation from one of her books. It can only be hoped that the final banknote meets with less opposition than its announcement did.

Grammar and vocabulary

4 Choose the correct answers (a–c).

Joseph Pulitzer: the legend lives on

You may well have heard of the Pulitzer Prizes for journalism and the arts, but what do you know about the man behind them? Born in Makó, Hungary, in 1847, Joseph Pulitzer was obsessed [1]___ the military and tried several times [2]___ the army. In 1864, he emigrated to the USA to become a soldier in the Civil War, and when it was over, he settled in St Louis, Missouri. He [3]___ there for long when he got a job as a reporter with a small German newspaper. Joseph was hard-working and ambitious, and he [4]___ work for sixteen hours a day most days. He bought newspapers and sold them at a profit. By 1883, he [5]___ a very wealthy man and he could afford [6]___ the *New York World*, a very prestigious newspaper. His new style of investigative journalism made the paper a success, although it also got him into trouble. In 1909, he was sued [7]___ after exposing an illegal payment by government officials. In the end, the case was dropped, but by then, Joseph was very ill. He was blind, depressed and extremely sensitive [8]___ , so he used [9]___ his paper from a private office on his yacht. This is where he [10]___ in 1911, leaving two million dollars to Columbia University in his will to found the first School of Journalism and establish the Pulitzer Prizes.

1	a about	b of	c with
2	a join	b to join	c joining
3	a didn't live	b wasn't living	c hadn't been living
4	a did	b had	c would
5	a had become	b did become	c had been becoming
6	a purchase	b to purchase	c purchasing
7	a for libel	b at libel	c to libel
8	a at noise	b to noise	c with noise
9	a to manage	b managing	c to managing
10	a passed away	b passed by	c passed off

Writing

5 A newspaper has published an article asking which person of historical significance from your country should appear on the next issue of a banknote. Write a letter to the editor in which you:

- recommend who should appear on the banknote.
- explain the reasons for your choice.
- describe a remarkable event in the life of your chosen person.
- suggest a place, an activity and an object that illustrate the life of your chosen person.

Listening

1 **🎧 2.28** Listen and choose the correct answers (a–c).

1 Listen to the conversation. Why does the woman suggest going to the festival by coach?

a It's the most convenient way to go.

b It's the cheapest way to go.

c It's the most reliable way to go.

2 Listen to the speaker. What is his intention?

a To explain how to get tickets for a festival.

b To describe one of the best festivals in the UK.

c To persuade people to go to a festival.

3 Listen to the interview. How does the volunteer feel about his job?

a He's overwhelmed by the quantity of rubbish.

b He's proud of his group's contribution.

c He's disappointed by the lack of co-operation.

4 Listen to the news report. Which is the best headline?

a GLASTONBURY WEATHER BETTER THAN EVER

b FESTIVAL RAINED OFF YET AGAIN

c REVELLERS SET FOR SUNSHINE AND SHOWERS

5 Listen to the conversation. What is the mother's attitude?

a She's worried about her son staying in a tent.

b She's resigned to the fact her son is going to the festival.

c She's annoyed that her son already has a ticket.

Speaking

2 Work in pairs. A British exchange student is coming to stay with you when an important festival is on and has asked what happens during the event. Talk with him/her about the topics below.

accommodation   clothes   food and drink   what to see

Reading

3 Read the article. Match sentences A–G with gaps 1–5 in the article. There are two extra sentences.

A But others have continued, like the role of women as the head of the family and the community.

B Then, there's a website for children where they can learn more about Chickasaw history, people, culture and language through interactive games and activities.

C The use of new technologies and dynamic business strategies in a global market are also encouraged.

D She was the last remaining monolingual speaker of the Chickasaw language.

E The study of the arts and humanities is necessary to the success of the Chickasaw Nation.

F And if history is anything to go by, he isn't wrong.

G This led to the number of native speakers falling from around 3,000 in the 1960s to fewer than seventy today.

Using modern technology to preserve an ancient language

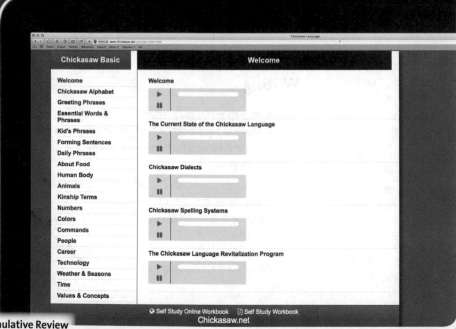

Monday 30 December 2013 was a tragic day for the people of the Chickasaw Nation. It was the day on which a 93-year-old member of the tribe called Emily Johnson Dickerson passed away. But Emily wasn't just any old member of the tribe. [1]__ Through her death, the tribe lost not only a beloved member of their extended family, but also a valuable source of knowledge about their language and culture.

The Chickasaw Nation is made up of around 57,000 people, most of whom live in the thirteen areas of Oklahoma, USA, that were once designated 'Indian Territory'. Their land is largely rural, but much of their way of life is modern – they use mobile phones, drive cars and have access to the internet. Some of the traditional Chickasaw customs have died out, such as native folk medicine. [2]___ The Chickasaw people are determined that their language should also continue.

There are currently 175 Native American languages spoken in the USA, but fewer than twenty are expected to survive the next one hundred years. The language of the Chickasaws, known as 'Chikashshanompa', has been in existence for well over three thousand years, but it is now in danger of disappearing. Young Chickasaws sent to government boarding schools in the past were discouraged from speaking their language and were obliged to learn English to negotiate with people outside the tribe. [3]___ Which is where the Chickasaw Language Revitalisation Programme comes in.

The aim of the programme is to keep the culture, language and oral traditions of the tribe alive, and it is using cutting-edge technology to do this. First, there is Chickasaw TV, an online network with a channel dedicated to learning the Chickasaw language through lessons, songs, games and stories. [4]___ But the programme's most remarkable achievement is its app: Chickasaw Language Basics. The app features hundreds of Chickasaw words, phrases, songs and videos, and it is the first of its kind to be developed by a tribe or a nation.

According to Joseph Hinson, director of the Department of Chickasaw Language, the Chickasaw are 'a pretty hard-headed, persistent people.' [5]___ The fifty-thousand-year-old indigenous Native American tribe has survived the Conquistadores, numerous wars with Europeans, the American Civil War, and compulsory removal from their native lands... and they're still here. One can only hope that the massive effort the tribe is putting into preserving their language succeeds, so that Chikashshanompa is not lost to the world forever.

Grammar and vocabulary

4 Read the text and choose the correct answers (a–c).

Don't stand so close to me

Researchers at the department of neuroscience at University College London [1]___ the limits of personal space. This is the area around a person which determines whether he or she is comfortable with the closeness of another person or whether the distance is causing them to feel [2]___ . Fifteen volunteers aged between twenty and thirty-seven chose [3]___ in the study, which involved receiving an electric shock to the hand. The volunteers [4]___ hold their hands at different distances from their face in order to receive the shock, and their reaction to it was measured by the scientists. The measurements were taken from the volunteers' eye movements, and in particular, how often they blinked. The more they blinked, [5]___ of a threat they felt the shock was to their face. The scientists [6]___ that the personal space of the volunteers appeared to have an abrupt boundary when they felt threatened, rather than having a gradual increase. The boundary varied among individuals, but it was generally between twenty and forty centimetres from their face. A spokesperson from the university said it is possible that the findings [7]___ be useful for helping police and other emergency personnel to assess threats [8]___ .

Personal space is thought to be a cultural issue because it is seen as being [9]___ important in other countries, such as China and India. The spokesperson said researchers hoped to study subjects from other countries soon to understand [10]___ the differences between cultures.

	a	b	c
1	have studied	studied	have been studying
2	on edge	at edge	in edge
3	take part	to take part	taking part
4	must	had to	should
5	the more	more	the most
6	had found	found	had been finding
7	could	can't	must
8	more accurately	most accurately	the most accurately
9	least	most	less
10	best	well	better

Writing

5 There are six thousand languages in the world, but linguists fear that 50% of them will become extinct within the next century. Write an essay in which you present the advantages and disadvantages of preserving endangered languages.

Listening

1 🎧 2.29 **Listen to a radio programme about therapy dogs. Choose the correct answer.**

1 Why does the presenter use the quote about animals at the start of the programme?
   a To show how affectionate they are.
   b To explain how considerate they are.
   c To illustrate how ignorant they are.
   d To emphasise how trusting they are.

2 According to Freya Wilcox, Alzheimer's patients are generally
   a easy-going.
   b insecure.
   c thick-skinned.
   d vain.

3 During the therapy dogs' visits, the patients tend to be
   a more sympathetic.
   b hungrier.
   c more upbeat.
   d more single-minded.

4 To be a therapy dog, an animal must
   a have the right personality.
   b know a lot of people.
   c be wary of strange noises.
   d understand body language.

5 Why do the dogs go home at night?
   a In order to spend some time with their trainers.
   b So as not to catch an illness from the patients.
   c To be clean and rested for the next day's work.
   d So that they don't disturb the patients.

Speaking

2 **Work in pairs. You want to give an elderly relative a pet to keep him or her company. Say which of these pets you would choose and why. Say why you are rejecting the other option.**

Reading

3 **Match texts A–C with questions 1–6 below. Some texts match with more than one question.**

Which meeting …
1 was held in order for an important question to be asked? ☐
2 lasted for less than an hour? ☐
3 involved people of different nationalities? ☐
4 was organised privately? ☐
5 involved the exchange of gifts? ☐
6 resulted in a long-term association between the participants? ☐

Three monumental meetings in history

A
On 4 May 1904, a meeting was held between two British businessmen that resulted in one of the most famous automobile partnerships in history.
After purchasing a car whose performance he was dissatisfied with, Frederick Henry Royce had succeeded in creating his own model that gave the occupants a quieter and smoother ride. One of these vehicles was purchased by Royce's colleague Henry Edmunds, who was friends with a car dealer in London called Charles Stewart Rolls. Edmunds showed Rolls his new car and arranged for Rolls and Royce to meet over lunch at the Midland Hotel in Manchester. The two men began doing business together, and on 15 March 1906, Rolls-Royce Limited was born. Unfortunately, the partnership ended rather abruptly four years later when Rolls was killed in a plane crash. However, the company continued, and the Rolls-Royce went on to become arguably one of the best cars in the world.

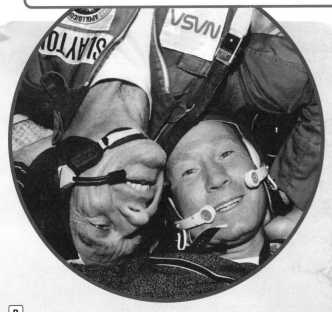

B

On 17 July 1975, a meeting occurred that a few years earlier would have been unthinkable. On that day, US astronaut Thomas Stafford and Russian cosmonaut Alexei Leonov exchanged the first international handshake in space. The Apollo–Soyuz Test Project, named after the two spacecraft involved, was a joint venture organised by the US and Soviet governments to demonstrate the improved relations between the two nations. The Apollo and the Soyuz were launched on 15 July within seven and a half hours of each other, and they met over France, where the two spacecraft joined. They stayed connected for nearly two days, long enough for the three Americans and two Soviets to visit each other's ships, conduct experiments together, share meals and converse in each other's languages. One of the gifts they exchanged was a bag of tree seeds which were later planted in the two countries.

C

On 27 March 1997, a rather awkward meeting took place before the press in a Tennessee state prison hospital. The participants were two men: Dexter King, son of the murdered civil rights activist Martin Luther King, and James Earl Ray, the man who had been convicted of the assassination. King was 36 when the meeting happened, and Ray was 69 and very sick – he had to be taken to the meeting room in a wheelchair. During the 25 minutes the two men spent together, King asked Ray if he had killed King's father. Ray, who confessed to the killing at the time of his arrest, but then withdrew his confession, replied that he hadn't, to which King responded, 'I believe you.' Whether Ray was the killer or the murder was a government conspiracy will always remain a mystery because Ray died of liver disease a year later in prison.

Grammar and vocabulary

4 Choose the correct answers (a–c).

HOW TO REPAIR
a friendship

¹__ friendships have wobbly moments, and it's quite normal for friends to fall out every now and then. The important thing is knowing what to do if, or when, this ²__ and you have an argument. In general, the sooner you try to repair the friendship, ³__, though you should not approach your friend until you have both had time to calm down. Under no circumstances ⁴__ your friend immediately afterwards and demand to speak to them. Bear in mind that he or she will ⁵__ just as hurt and offended as you are. Once you've managed to cool off, find somewhere quiet to sit down and think about how you're going to repair the friendship. A face-to-face meeting is always the best, although there's a danger your friend might ⁶__ your offer to speak at first. However, it's very unlikely that they will stop speaking to you ⁷__, so it's worth trying again on another occasion. When you start the conversation, you need to apologise for the way you have acted, even if you weren't the person ⁸__ . There's no point in lecturing your friend ⁹__ their behaviour as this approach won't work. A useful way to continue is to ¹⁰__ a good memory to share with your friend. Once you find yourselves on common ground, the conversation should flow more easily, and you'll be able to talk about whatever it is that made you fall out in the first place.

1 a All	**b** All the	**c** Each of
2 a happen	**b** happens	**c** will happen
3 a best	**b** better	**c** the better
4 a you should call	**b** call you	**c** should you call
5 a be feeling	**b** feeling	**c** have felt
6 a turn away	**b** turn down	**c** turn off
7 a at last	**b** for good	**c** in effect
8 a at fault	**b** by mistake	**c** in doubt
9 a about	**b** for	**c** in
10 a bring about	**b** bring in	**c** bring up

Writing

5 Some people say that you can't be friends with a person you hardly ever see. Write an essay in which you give your opinion of this view and show how a friendship of yours illustrates this.

Cumulative Review 4 (Units I–7)

Listening

1 🎧 **2.30** Listen to a radio programme about the Ponzi scheme. Decide if the sentences are true (T) or false (F).

1 A Ponzi scheme is a way of deceiving investors. ☐

2 The first ever Ponzi scheme was run by Charles Ponzi. ☐

3 Ponzi set up his scheme as soon as he arrived in the USA. ☐

4 The scheme involved the buying and exchanging of International Reply Coupons. ☐

5 Ponzi's scheme was illegal right from the start. ☐

6 At the height of the scheme, Ponzi was making a quarter of a million dollars a day. ☐

7 Ponzi's investors wanted to leave the scheme when the police began investigating his company. ☐

8 Ponzi was sent back to the country of his birth on his release from prison. ☐

Speaking

2 Work in pairs. You've lost your school bag containing all your books. You think you left it on the train. Report the loss to the train company. In the conversation, discuss the following points:

1 the circumstances of losing the bag

2 a description of the bag

3 what was in the bag

4 what will happen next

Reading

3 Read the text below and choose the correct answers.

1 The most shocking thing about Amina Arraf is that

a she disappeared and remains missing.

b she wasn't a real person.

c she wasn't afraid to express her views online.

d she was very close to an American man.

Who are you?

On 6 June 2011, the media reported the kidnapping of a female Syrian–American blogger called Amina Arraf. Regarded as a daring political rebel, the 35-year-old had become popular for her blogs protesting about the lack of freedom in Syria, where she was supposedly living at the time. Yet only two days after her disappearance, it was discovered that Amina had never existed at all. She was a fictional character created by a forty-year-old American man called Tom MacMaster, a PhD student at the University of Edinburgh.

MacMaster's invention of the blogger is an example of sock puppetry: the use of false identities to deceive others. The false identity is known as a sock puppet, and its creator, a puppet master. MacMaster created Amina to enable him to express his strong views on Middle-Eastern affairs without offending other Americans, who may not have approved. Writing as Amina Arraf gave him the authority to be able to say what he wanted to. But this is not the only reason for using sock puppetry.

At the turn of the millennium, an American woman named Debbie Swenson created the fictional character Kaycee Nicole, a teenage girl suffering from terminal cancer. Her blog, Living Colours, described in detail Kaycee's fight for survival, and it attracted millions of readers. When Kaycee 'died' on 14 May 2001, her fans were devastated. But their distress turned to anger when they discovered that Kaycee was not a real person. The character had been developed by Ms Swenson to get the attention and sympathy she craved.

2 The reason why Tom MacMaster blogged under a false identity was
   a to find out what his fellow countrymen and women thought.
   b to deceive people into taking sides with the USA.
   c to appeal to both men and women in the Middle East.
   d to give credibility to his radical ideas.

3 Debbie Swenson created Kaycee Nicole because
   a she enjoyed sharing her medical knowledge.
   b she wanted advice on how to treat her daughter's illness.
   c she needed to feel popular with other people.
   d she felt like showing her support for cancer sufferers.

4 The sock puppet Mary Rosh was used by John Lott
   a to give him the voice of authority.
   b to criticise his opponents.
   c to make out that he was married.
   d to encourage others to look on his work favourably.

5 The writer of the article concludes that
   a everybody should be wary of people they come across online.
   b the police should create more sock puppets to combat crime.
   c social media sites are safer than they used to be.
   d terrorists pose a bigger threat on the internet than they do in real life.

While Amina and Kaycee were used as a means to meet the needs of their creators, other identities have been invented to make a profit. American gun advocate John Lott made up a fake student, Mary Rosh, to defend his writing online and give him positive reviews. Mystery writer RJ Ellory went further and fabricated a whole team of sock puppets, not only to praise his own books, but also to criticise those of his rivals. Well-respected British historian Orlando Figes lost face completely when he had to publicly apologise for doing the same.

Yet none of these stories can compete with the large-scale sock puppetry in existence today. It is understood that the New York City Police Department has several false identities hanging out on social media sites in order to catch criminals. The US military is said to have a number of sock puppets online searching for potential terrorists. While most of us are unlikely to have dealings with these organisations, the stories of Amina, Kaycee and the fake reviewers are much closer to home. It is clear that the internet is a minefield today and we all have to step very carefully in order not to get hurt.

Grammar and vocabulary

4 Choose the correct answers (a–c).

Don't be deceived!

Celebrated in many countries on 1 April, April Fools Day is a day on which people are encouraged [1]___ practical jokes on their friends and family. The press often joins in the fun by [2]___ fictional stories to print on the day. One of the most extensive April Fools stories ever published was a seven-page supplement about a fictional island nation that appeared in the *Guardian* newspaper back in 1977. The feature was [3]___ as a serious report celebrating the tenth anniversary of the nation's independence. The idea was conceived by the *Guardian*'s special reports team, one of whom suggested [4]___ the nation 'San Serriffe', after the sans-serif printing style of letters used in newspapers. In fact, the team [5]___ the readers' lack of knowledge in publishing by using these words as names for all the places mentioned in the supplement. At the time, computers had not yet entered the home, so most readers had never heard them before and were completely [6]___ by the report. Those who were familiar with the words realised immediately that the feature was a joke and [7]___ to the editor. The newspaper received a number of complaints from travel agencies, however, for [8]___ that San Serriffe was a tourist destination. It appears that some of their customers believed in the existence [9]___ the islands and wanted to see them for themselves. Apparently, several people had called in to ask how much [10]___ to book a holiday there.

1 a	play	b playing	c to play
2 a	bringing up	b making up	c turning up
3 a	let on	b owned up	c passed off
4 a	call	b calling	c to call
5 a	played on	b set up	c zoomed in
6 a	got over	b put down	c taken in
7 a	gave a thumbs up	b pursed their lips	c raised their eyebrows
8 a	asking out	b going out	c making out
9 a	of	b for	c by
10 a	does it cost	b it cost	c did it cost

Writing

5 You have read an article about the dangers of using social media. Write an article for your school website about the risks associated with using social media and propose ways of persuading young people to use it responsibly.

Cumulative Review 5 (Units I–9)

Listening

1 🎧 2.31 Listen to four speakers talking about their favourite TV advertisement. Match speakers 1–4 with sentences A–E. There is one extra sentence.

A He/She recognises a familiar scene in the ad. ☐
B He/She admires the technique used to make the ad. ☐
C He/She praises the clever slogan at the end of the ad. ☐
D He/She enjoys seeing somebody made happy in the ad. ☐
E He/She empathises with one of the characters in the ad. ☐

Speaking

2 You want to advertise a fundraising event your school is holding. Say which of these places is the best for advertising the event and why. Say why you are rejecting the other option.

Reading

3 Read the article. Match sentences A–G with gaps 1–5 in the article. There are two extra sentences.

A As a result, Kuapa Kokoo received only half of the cocoa they had paid for and had no money left to buy more.

B The income they received from cocoa was vital for paying for school fees and medical costs.

C Now the company comprises around 85,000 small-scale farmers, and it has its own chocolate brand, Divine.

D Then, they replaced all of the weighing scales to ensure that they hadn't been fixed to give the farmers a lower price.

E This time, they received a much larger loan to work with and the banks were back to normal, so the farmers could cash their cheques.

F As the weeks progressed, recorders began to hire their own private trucks, taking on more responsibility.

G Genuinely concerned about poorer farmers, he recruited experienced cocoa people, who he knew and trusted, and found an office for the company in the city of Kumasi.

SUCCESSFUL ETHICAL TRADING: KUAPA KOKOO

Most people in the cocoa business used to laugh at the idea that farmers could have their own company. That was before the cocoa farmers' co-operative Kuapa Kokoo – literally 'best farmer cocoa' – was established in Ghana in 1993. ¹___ It is one of the most successful members of the fair trade group, the movement that promotes ethical trading. But the situation hasn't always been like this.

International development agencies became aware of the need for a company protecting small farmers in Ghana when the government was obliged to hand over control of the cocoa trade to private companies. Kuapa Kokoo was set up under the management of Nana Frimpong, who was an engineer and a farmer, and also a friend of the Ghanaian President. ²___ Kuapa Kokoo now had a base and a team.

The first challenge facing the new company was corruption, which the management refused to tolerate. First, they made contact with independent recorders in each village – that is, the people who manage the relationship with the farmers and take the cocoa to be weighed. ³___ Finally, they trained the recorders to the same level as the government's quality control officers,

who had previously looked down on them and declared the produce low quality unless they were given a 'tip'. It looked as if Kuapa Kokoo was ready to do business.

The next problem was money – or lack of it. The cheques the company had been planning to pay the farmers with could not be exchanged for cash because the regional banks had run out of banknotes. So the Kuapa management had to withdraw from the bank in Ghanaian currency most of the £100,000 loan they had been given. Because of the competitive trading environment in the villages at the time, there was much confusion over the cocoa that had been promised to each company. ⁴___ The first season had been an absolute disaster.

Fortunately, the company had the support of the agencies to try again the following year. ⁵___ The company's new 'Pick Up and Pay' system, by which the recorders from each village would collect the cocoa and receive payment for it every two weeks, was a success. At the end of the second season, Kuapa Kokoo was officially identified as the most efficient of the new cocoa companies. Since then, it has never looked back.

Grammar and vocabulary

4 Choose the correct answers (a–c).

What a load of rubbish!

Freeganism is the practice of reusing things ¹___ by other people. Freegans may or may not be able to ²___ these things themselves, but that really isn't the point. The reason they look for things to recycle is to protest ³___ the consumer society we live in and also to be more ecological. ⁴___ concerns freegans the most is the quantity of food and drink that is wasted each year, which amounts to around 4.2 million tonnes in the UK alone. This figure is likely to rise ⁵___ people start to pay more attention to the purchases they make. Supermarket food has often been flown by plane, driven in trucks and packaged in unnecessary plastic before it appears on the shelves. The less food we have to produce, the ⁶___ natural resources we will use up. Not surprisingly, supermarkets would prefer freegans ⁷___ through their bins, which are usually located on private land. For this reason, police cars often ⁸___ outside to make sure there is no one around. If a police officer does find someone looking for food, he or she will usually ⁹___ and send them on their way. For freegans, however, the real crime is throwing away so much food and drink in the first place. They say that if the unwanted products ¹⁰___ properly, then nobody would have to go through supermarket bins.

1	a to discard	b discarded	c discarding
2	a afford	b budget	c haggle
3	a against	b for	c with
4	a All	b It	c What
5	a even if	b supposing	c unless
6	a fewer	b less	c little
7	a don't go	b not going	c not to go
8	a come across	b pull up	c stop over
9	a put them off	b tell off them	c tell them off
10	a are distributed	b were distributed	c would be distributed

Writing

5 A newspaper recently published an article about the fair trade movement suggesting that young people don't usually buy fair trade products. Write a letter to the editor where you express your opinion about this, suggesting ways of making these products more accessible to young people.

Writing Bank

For and against essay

Many young adults choose to leave their parents' home in order to share a house with friends.
Write an essay in which you present arguments for and against this course of action.

In the past, most people lived with their parents until they got married. But in the modern world, it is more common to leave home and share accommodation with friends. This choice has both positive and negative aspects.

There are several advantages to sharing with friends. Firstly, it gives you the opportunity to spend time with your friends and to build strong relationships with them. Secondly, it allows you to develop some of the practical skills that you will need as an independent adult. For instance, you will learn how to manage household bills, how to shop and cook, and so on. And thirdly, it makes living in your own home more affordable, and the more people who share, the more cost-effective it is. For instance, a shared house for six people is far cheaper than two houses for three people.

On the other hand, sharing a home has its disadvantages. Sharing a house can often cause disagreements. For instance, housemates often argue about household chores. What is more, it can be difficult to have time alone when you need it. And finally, the houses which young people share are sometimes in poor condition and landlords are not always good at repairing appliances when they break down.

Although sharing a house with other young people is not always easy, the advantages definitely outweigh the problems. It is certainly something I would like to do in a few years' time.

- The first paragraph should be the introduction. Include a thesis statement, which summarises the main issue.

- The second paragraph should focus on the advantages. Include at least two arguments, if possible.

- Give examples where appropriate, introduced by phrases like *For example, ...* or *For instance, ...*

- The third paragraph should focus on the disadvantages. Include at least two arguments, if possible.

- Begin the third paragraph with a phrase like *On the other hand, ...* or *However, ...* to express contrast with statements in the previous paragraph.

- The fourth paragraph should be the conclusion. State your own opinion and decide whether the arguments for outweigh the arguments against the thesis statement, or the other way around.

Article

According to the media, young people today are more interested in protests than in traditional party politics. Write an article for your local newspaper in which you give possible reasons for this preference and describe a protest which you personally witnessed or took part in.

- Choose a good title for your article.

- Start your article by getting the reader's attention. You can begin with a direct question or with a deliberately provocative statement.

- Include occasional questions where appropriate to make your style more engaging.

- Write in a simple, clear style that is appropriate to the publication (newspaper, magazine, etc.). Avoid language that is too formal or too colloquial.

- Make sure you cover all parts of the task. It is usually a good idea to put them in separate paragraphs.

AN APPETITE FOR ACTIVISM

Young people today only care about social media, music and fashion – or at least, that's the impression you get from the media. But in fact, this description is far from the truth. Young people are interested in important issues and want to make the world a better place. But they prefer direct action to party politics. What are the reasons for this?

The first reason is the simplest: most teenagers are still too young to vote, so why should they take an interest in party politics? But there are other factors too. When young people look at traditional politics, they don't find answers to the questions that are most important to them. How can we put an end to poverty? How can we save the world from pollution and global warming? But there are other organisations that address these topics directly. They arrange protests and other forms of activism. What is more, they use social media and the internet to publicise their campaigns, so it is easy for young people to find out about them.

Last month, I attended a protest against the building of a new retail park. Many of the protestors were under the age of twenty. We met near the proposed construction site and then marched into town, finishing outside the town hall. We stayed there all afternoon, giving out leaflets and talking to members of the public. It was a very successful protest and we even appeared on the local TV news.

Writing Bank

Opinion essay

Many people believe that it is to too late to reverse the harm which humans have done to the planet. Write an essay in which you present your opinion on this topic and suggest how people could limit further damage to the environment.

- Write in an appropriately formal style, avoiding colloquial words and expressions.

- The first paragraph should be an introduction. Include your thesis statement, which is a summary of your opinion on the issue.

- The second paragraph should focus on the first part of the task (presenting your opinion).

- Use appropriate linking words or phrases like *Additionally*, ... or *However*, ... to connect your ideas in a logical way.

- Give examples where appropriate, introduced by phrases like *For example*, ... , *For instance*, ... and *such as* ... .

- The third paragraph should focus on the second part of the task (making suggestions).

- The fourth paragraph should be the conclusion. Restate your opinion from paragraph 1, but do not repeat it word for word.

For many decades, humans have been damaging the environment by polluting the atmosphere and the oceans. Global warming threatens to change the planet's climate forever and make large areas of it uninhabitable. In my opinion, it is impossible to reverse all of this damage, but we can certainly make a positive difference by changing our behaviour.

In recent years, there has been some progress in preventing pollution. For example, factories and car engines are far cleaner than they were fifty years ago. Additionally, some products that harm the atmosphere, such as aerosols that contain dangerous chemicals, are no longer available. However, some forms of pollution are more difficult to tackle. Plastic waste will remain in the environment for thousands of years. And although governments are attempting to limit carbon emissions, nobody is certain whether this will be enough to stop global warming. But it is important to remain positive and do everything we can to prevent further damage to our planet.

It is perfectly possible for individuals to limit their own impact on the environment. For example, they should save electricity by switching off lights, computers and other electrical appliances when they are not using them. As far as possible, they should avoid buying products with plastic packaging and drink water from a reusable bottle.

In conclusion, I would say that we should all do what we can to prevent more damage to our environment. However, only time will tell whether this is enough to reverse the harm that has already been done.

Formal letter (complaint)

You and your family recently celebrated a special occasion in a small hotel, but were unhappy with the experience. Write a letter of complaint to the hotel manager in which you describe what went wrong and suggest how the hotel could improve its service to customers.

Dear Sir or Madam,

I am writing to complain about a recent stay at the White Deer Hotel in Broadford between 8 and 10 May. The holiday had been arranged to celebrate my grandfather's 75th birthday and involved twelve family members. Unfortunately, the service we received from your hotel was completely inadequate and prevented us from enjoying what should have been a very special occasion.

Our problems began as soon as we arrived. The check-in process took more than an hour and it appeared the hotel was not expecting us, even though I had phoned the week before to confirm our reservation. After that, things went from bad to worse. For example, we had asked that my grandparents be given a superior double room. In fact, they were given a standard room overlooking the car park at the back of the hotel. When we complained, we were told that the hotel was full and a change of rooms was impossible.

May I suggest that in future the hotel makes better preparations for special events of this kind? You should make guests feel welcome from the moment they arrive. I also believe that your check-in procedure needs to be improved. For example, at busy times, more than one receptionist should be at the desk.

I expect to receive an explanation for our unsatisfactory treatment and would appreciate an offer of compensation. I look forward to your reply.

Yours faithfully

M Wright

Mark Wright

- If you do not know the name of the person you are writing to, begin with *Dear Sir or Madam*.

- Begin your letter by saying why you are writing.

- Write in an appropriately formal style, avoiding colloquial words and expressions.

- The next paragraph should focus on the first part of the task (describing the situation). Remember to include details and examples.

- The following paragraph should focus on the second part of the task (making suggestions).

- End the main part of the letter by stating clearly what you expect to happen next.

- If the letter began with *Dear Sir or Madam*, it should end *Yours faithfully*, and your signature. (However, you end with *Yours sincerely*, before your signature if you addressed the recipient by name at the start.)

F Functions Bank

Speculating and deducing

I can't be sure, but ... (1G)

It looks like some kind of ... or maybe a ... (1G)

It looks to me like a ... of some kind. (1G)

It's / There's a sort of ... (1G)

It's / They're most likely a ... or something like that. (1G)

I'd say that ... (1G)

He's yawning, so he must be tired or bored. (5G)

She's laughing, so she can't be sad. (5G)

He may / might / could be lonely. (5G)

It looks as if ... (5G)

The photo appears to show (a canteen). (5G)

She looks like a (nice person). (5G)

Judging by (their expressions), I'd say that ... (5G)

I can't be certain, but ... (5G)

I might be wrong, but ... (5G)

The boy seems to be (writing something). (5G)

Being diplomatic

Can I have a word with you about ... ? (2G)

Well, it's just that ... (2G)

What did you have in mind? (2G)

I thought perhaps we could ... (2G)

You must feel that ... (2G)

So, how can we resolve this? (2G)

I didn't want to bring it up, but ... (2G)

You should have said something earlier. (2G)

And could we possibly agree on ... ? (2G)

Presenting one side of the argument

The first / second advantage ... (2H)

It can be argued that ... (2H)

No one can deny that ... (2H)

On the one hand, ... (2H)

It is also true that ... (2H)

Furthermore, / Moreover, ... (2H)

Some people claim / believe that ... (8H)

It is said that ... (8H)

There are a number of arguments for ... (8H)

It is sometimes argued that ... (8H)

Presenting the other side of the argument

However, ... (2H)

On the other hand, ... (2H)

Although it is true that ... , we should also remember that ... (2H)

Having said that, ... / That said, ... (2H)

And yet, ... (2H)

Some people take the opposite view ... (8H)

Opponents claim that ... (8H)

Moving onto another topic

I'd like to know / ask / hear about ... (3G)

Let's move on to ... (3G)

There's something else I'd like to talk / ask about, and that's ... (3G)

That brings me on to the subject of ... (3G)

Could I also ask you about ... ? (3G)

Is there anything else I should know about? (3G)

Paraphrasing

I'm not sure how to say it in English ... (3G)

I don't know what it's called in English ... (3G)

In other words ... (3G)

What I mean is ... (3G)

It's something you (use for) ... (3G)

It's a kind / sort of ... (3G)

Making a selection

I think I'll choose ... mainly because ... (4G)

I'm opting for ... and that's because ... (4G)

The best option would be the ... because ... (4G)

The reason why I'm (not) choosing the ... is that ... (4G)

I wouldn't go for the ... basically because ... (4G)

I wouldn't pick the ... for the reason that ... (4G)

Pausing for thought

Hmm, let me think. (5G)

Let me see what I can come up with. (5G)

I need a minute to recall ... (5G)

Nothing springs immediately to mind. (5G)

I suppose the last time was ... (5G)

I seem to remember it was in / at / on ... (5G)

F Functions Bank

Presenting opinions

There's no doubt in my mind that ... (6F)

As far as I'm concerned ... (6F)

I believe very strongly that ... (6F)

I'm absolutely convinced that ... (6F)

Nobody can deny that ... (6F)

It's perfectly clear that ... (6F)

In my view, ... (9C)

Personally, ... (9C)

As I see it, ... (9C)

To my mind, ... (9C)

My impression is ... (9C)

I've a feeling that ... (9C)

I strongly believe ... (9C)

Asking for clarification

Sorry, do you think you could repeat that? (6G)

I'm afraid I didn't quite catch that. (6G)

Would you mind saying that again? (6G)

What do you mean by ... ? (6G)

Is that something like ... ? (6G)

Is that the same ... ? (6G)

Expressing a firm opinion

To my mind, ... (8G)

In my opinion, ... (8G)

I'm of the opinion that ... (8G)

I feel quite strongly that ... (8G)

It is clear to me that ... (8G)

I firmly believe that ... (8G)

Counter claim and rebuttal

People might say that ... , but I believe ... (8G)

It could be argued that ... . However, it seems to me that, ... (8G)

Some people see it differently. For example, ... But I don't agree. (8G)

While it's true that ... , I feel that ... (8G)

While this is a fair point, I don't think that ... (8G)

Summing up / Giving your opinion

In conclusion, ... (8H)

All things considered, ... (8H)

To sum up, ... (8H)

On balance, ... (8H)

All in all, ... (8H)

In my view / opinion, ... (8H)

Introducing a fact

Actually, ... (9C)

In fact, ... (9C)

In reality, ... (9C)

The truth is ... (9C)

It's true that ... (9C)

It's undeniable that ... (9C)

Undeniably ... (9C)

It's been proved that ... (9C)

Justifying your opinion

The reason I think that is because ... (9G)

The main reason is that ... (9G)

Another thing is that ... (9G)

On top of that, ... (9G)

I definitely think that the ... is better, because ... (9G)

For those reasons I think that ... (9G)

Expressing a tentative opinion

I don't have any strong opinions about ... (9G)

I'm not sure about that. Let me think. (9G)

It could be argued that ... (9G)

There might be a case for arguing that ... (9G)

Thinking about it, I suppose that ... (9G)

Wordlist

Unit I

accuse (v)	/əˈkjuːz/
addicted (to) (adj)	/əˈdɪktɪd/
(be an) adult (n)	/əˈdʌlt/
advise (v)	/ədˈvaɪz/
afford (v)	/əˈfɔːd/
apologise (v)	/əˈpɒlədʒaɪz/
ask (v)	/ɑːsk/
aware (of) (adj)	/əˈweə/
be born (v)	/bi bɔːn/
be brought up (by) (phr v)	/bi brɔːt ʌp/
become a grandparent (v)	/bɪˈkʌm ə ˈgrænpeərənt/
beg (v)	/beg/
buy a house or flat (v)	/baɪ ə haʊs ɔː flæt/
(be a) centenarian (n)	/ˌsentɪˈneəriən/
choose (v)	/tʃuːz/
continue (v)	/kənˈtɪnjuː/
curious (about) (adj)	/ˈkjʊəriəs/
decide (v)	/dɪˈsaɪd/
deny (v)	/dɪˈnaɪ/
(be) elderly (adj)	/ˈeldəli/
emigrate (v)	/ˈemɪgreɪt/
end up (v)	/end ʌp/
expect (v)	/ɪkˈspekt/
fall in love (v)	/fɔːl ɪn lʌv/
forget (v)	/fəˈget/
get divorced (v)	/get dɪˈvɔːst/
get engaged (v)	/get ɪnˈgeɪdʒd/
get married (v)	/get ˈmærid/
get your first job (v)	/get jɔː fɜːst dʒɒb/
go on (v)	/gəʊ ɒn/
go to university (v)	/gəʊ tə ˌjuːnɪˈvɜːsəti/
good (at) (adj)	/gʊd/
grow up (phr v)	/grəʊ ʌp/
have a change of career (v)	/həv ə tʃeɪndʒ ɒv kəˈrɪə/
hope (v)	/həʊp/
(be an) infant (n)	/ˈɪnfənt/
inherit (money, a house, etc.) (v)	/ɪnˈherɪt/
insist on (v)	/ɪnˈsɪst ɒn/
keep (v)	/kiːp/
learn to drive (v)	/lɜːn tə draɪv/
leave home (v)	/liːv həʊm/
leave school (v)	/liːv skuːl/
like (v)	/laɪk/
manage (v)	/ˈmænɪdʒ/
mention (v)	/ˈmenʃn/
(be) middle-aged (adj)	/ˈmɪdl ˈeɪdʒd/
mind (v)	/maɪnd/
move house (v)	/muːv haʊs/
obsessed (with) (adj)	/əbˈsest/
offer (v)	/ˈɒfə/
pass away (phr v)	/pɑːs əˈweɪ/
persuade (v)	/pəˈsweɪd/
prefer (v)	/prɪˈfɜː/
promise (v)	/ˈprɒmɪs/
propose (v)	/prəˈpəʊz/
remember (v)	/rɪˈmembə/
remind of (v)	/rɪˈmaɪnd ɒv/
retire (v)	/rɪˈtaɪə/
sensitive (to) (adj)	/ˈsensətɪv/
settle down (phr v)	/ˈsetl daʊn/
shocked (about) (adj)	/ʃɒkt/
spend (v)	/spend/
split up (phr v)	/splɪt ʌp/
start (v)	/stɑːt/
start a business (v)	/stɑːt ə ˈbɪznəs/
start a family (v)	/stɑːt ə ˈfæməli/
start school (v)	/stɑːt skuːl/
stop (v)	/stɒp/
suggest (v)	/səˈdʒest/
(be in your) teens (n)	/tiːnz/
tell (v)	/tel/
thank for (v)	/θæŋk fɔː/
(be a) toddler (n)	/ˈtɒdlə/
try (v)	/traɪ/
unhappy (with) (adj)	/ʌnˈhæpi/
want (v)	/wɒnt/
warn (v)	/wɔːn/

Unit 1

a bit (adv)	/ə bɪt/
absolutely (adv)	/ˌæbsəˈluːtli/
accessibility (n)	/əkˌsesəˈbɪləti/
affectionate (adj)	/əˈfekʃənət/
afraid (adj)	/əˈfreɪd/
alive (adj)	/əˈlaɪv/
alone (adj)	/əˈləʊn/
angry (adj)	/ˈæŋgri/
annoyed (adj)	/əˈnɔɪd/
asleep (adj)	/əˈsliːp/
astonished (adj)	/əˈstɒnɪʃt/
awful (adj)	/ˈɔːfl/
bad-mannered (adj)	/ˌbæd ˈmænəd/
bad-tempered (adj)	/ˌbæd ˈtempəd/
be in the public eye (v)	/bi ɪn ðə ˈpʌblɪk aɪ/
be in the public interest (v)	/bi ɪn ðə ˈpʌblɪk ˈɪntrəst/
bossy (adj)	/ˈbɒsi/
cautious (adj)	/ˈkɔːʃəs/
celebrities (n)	/səˈlebrətiz/
considerate (adj)	/kənˈsɪdərət/
content (n)	/kənˈtent/
creative (adj)	/kriˈeɪtɪv/
critical (adj)	/ˈkrɪtɪkl/
cruel (adj)	/ˈkruːəl/
delighted (adj)	/dɪˈlaɪtɪd/
easy-going (adj)	/ˌiːziˈgəʊɪŋ/
eccentric (adj)	/ɪkˈsentrɪk/
ecstatic (adj)	/ɪkˈstætɪk/
exhausted (adj)	/ɪgˈzɔːstɪd/
extremely (adv)	/ɪkˈstriːmli/
fascinated (adj)	/ˈfæsɪneɪtɪd/
feedback (n)	/ˈfiːdbæk/
free press (n)	/friː pres/
frightened (adj)	/ˈfraɪtnd/
furious (adj)	/ˈfjʊəriəs/
glad (adj)	/glæd/
happy (adj)	/ˈhæpi/
harass (v)	/ˈhærəs/
hardworking (adj)	/ˌhɑːd ˈwɜːkɪŋ/
hilarious (adj)	/hɪˈleəriəs/
industrious (adj)	/ɪnˈdʌstriəs/
insecure (adj)	/ˌɪnsɪˈkjʊə/
interaction (n)	/ˌɪntərˈækʃn/
invade someone's privacy (v)	/ɪnˈveɪd ˈsʌmwʌnz ˈprɪvəsi/
investigative journalism (n)	/ɪnˈvestɪgətɪv ˈdʒɜːnəlɪzəm/
journalist (n)	/ˈdʒɜːnəlɪst/
light-hearted (adj)	/ˌlaɪt ˈhɑːtɪd/
living (adj)	/ˈlɪvɪŋ/
lonely (adj)	/ˈləʊnli/
miserable (adj)	/ˈmɪzrəbl/
open-minded (adj)	/ˌəʊpən ˈmaɪndɪd/
outgoing (adj)	/ˈaʊtgəʊɪŋ/

Wordlist

paparazzi (n)	/ˌpæpəˈrætsi/	
passionate (adj)	/ˈpæʃənət/	
press regulators (n)	/pres ˈregjuleɪtəz/	
privacy laws (n)	/ˈprɪvəsi lɔːz/	
provider (n)	/prəˈvaɪdə/	
publicity scandal (n)	/pʌbˈlɪsəti ˈskændl/	
pushy (adj)	/ˈpʊʃi/	
quick-witted (adj)	/ˌkwɪk ˈwɪtɪd/	
self-confident (adj)	/ˌself ˈkɒnfɪdənt/	
selfless (adj)	/ˈselfləs/	
shrewd (adj)	/ʃruːd/	
single-minded (adj)	/ˌsɪŋgl ˈmaɪndɪd/	
sleeping (adj)	/ˈsliːpɪŋ/	
spontaneous (adj)	/spɒnˈteɪniəs/	
stalk (v)	/stɔːk/	
starving (adj)	/ˈstɑːvɪŋ/	
stingy (adj)	/ˈstɪndʒi/	
subscriber (n)	/səbˈskraɪbə/	
sue for libel (v)	/suː fə ˈlaɪbl/	
sympathetic (adj)	/ˌsɪmpəˈθetɪk/	
tabloid press (n)	/ˌtæblɔɪd ˈpres/	
terrible (adj)	/ˈterəbl/	
terrified (adj)	/ˈterɪfaɪd/	
the press (n)	/ðə pres/	
thick-skinned (adj)	/θɪk ˈskɪnd/	
thrilled (adj)	/θrɪld/	
totally (adv)	/ˈtəʊtəli/	
untrustworthy (adj)	/ʌnˈtrʌstwɜːði/	
vain (adj)	/veɪn/	
very (adv)	/ˈveri/	
well behaved (adj)	/ˌwel bɪˈheɪvd/	
wonderful (adj)	/ˈwʌndəfl/	

Unit 2

alarmed (adj)	/əˈlɑːmd/	
amused (adj)	/əˈmjuːzd/	
anxious (adj)	/ˈæŋkʃəs/	
ashamed (adj)	/əˈʃeɪmd/	
at fault	/ət fɔːlt/	
at first	/ət fɜːst/	
at once	/ət wʌns/	
at stake	/ət steɪk/	
be down in the dumps	/bi daʊn ɪn ðə dʌmps/	
be fuming	/bi fjuːmɪŋ/	
be green with envy	/bi griːn wɪð ˈenvi/	
be in two minds about something	/bi ɪn tuː maɪndz əˈbaʊt ˈsʌmθɪŋ/	
be on edge	/bi ɒn edʒ/	
be over the moon	/bi ˈəʊvə(r) ðə muːn/	
be tearing your hair out	/bi ˈteərɪŋ jɔː heə(r) aʊt/	
bitter (adj)	/ˈbɪtə/	
blow your top	/bləʊ jɔː tɒp/	
by mistake	/baɪ mɪˈsteɪk/	
combat (v)	/ˈkɒmbæt/	
commit (v)	/kəˈmɪt/	
content (adj)	/kənˈtent/	
cut (v)	/kʌt/	
deter (v)	/dɪˈtɜː/	
disappointed (adj)	/ˌdɪsəˈpɔɪntɪd/	
disillusioned (adj)	/ˌdɪsɪˈluːʒnd/	
envious (adj)	/ˈenviəs/	
exasperated (adj)	/ɪgˈzæspəreɪtɪd/	
for good	/fə ˈgʊd/	
frustrated (adj)	/frʌˈstreɪtɪd/	
furious (adj)	/ˈfjʊəriəs/	
humiliated (adj)	/hjuːˈmɪlieɪtɪd/	
hysterical (adj)	/hɪˈsterɪkl/	
in common	/ɪn ˈkɒmən/	

in fact	/ɪn fækt/	
in trouble	/ɪn ˈtrʌbl/	
indecisive (adj)	/ˌɪndɪˈsaɪsɪv/	
irritated (adj)	/ˈɪrɪteɪtɪd/	
lose face	/luːz feɪs/	
miserable (adj)	/ˈmɪzrəbl/	
of course	/ɒv kɔːs/	
on purpose	/ɒn ˈpɜːpəs/	
petty (adj)	/ˈpeti/	
prevention (n)	/prɪˈvenʃn/	
record (v)	/rɪˈkɔːd/	
something gets on your nerves	/ˈsʌmθɪŋ gets ɒn jɔː nɜːvz/	
stressed (adj)	/strest/	
stunned (adj)	/stʌnd/	
under age	/ˈʌndəreɪdʒ/	
upbeat (adj)	/ˈʌpbiːt/	
violent (adj)	/ˈvaɪələnt/	
wave (n)	/weɪv/	

Unit 3

annoyance (n)	/əˈnɔɪəns/	
anxiety (n)	/æŋˈzaɪəti/	
bill (n)	/bɪl/	
biscuit (n)	/ˈbɪskɪt/	
bite your fingernails (v)	/baɪt jɔː ˈfɪŋgəneɪlz/	
boredom (n)	/ˈbɔːdəm/	
bow your head (v)	/baʊ jɔː hed/	
candy (n)	/ˈkændi/	
cell phone (n)	/ˈselfəʊn/	
check (n)	/tʃek/	
clear your throat (v)	/klɪə(r) jɔː θrəʊt/	
confusion (n)	/kənˈfjuːʒn/	
cookie (n)	/ˈkʊki/	
cough (v)	/kɒf/	
cover your mouth (v)	/ˈkʌvə(r) jɔː maʊð/	
cross your fingers (v)	/krɒs jɔː ˈfɪŋgəz/	
cross your legs (v)	/krɒs jɔː legz/	
deep-throated (adj)	/diːp ˈθrəʊtɪd/	
disapproval (n)	/ˌdɪsəˈpruːvl/	
disgust (n)	/dɪsˈgʌst/	
event (n)	/ɪˈvent/	
exchange presents (v)	/ɪksˈtʃeɪndʒ ˈpreznts/	
family gathering (n)	/ˈfæməli ˈgæðərɪŋ/	
fear (n)	/fɪə/	
fidget (v)	/ˈfɪdʒɪt/	
film (n)	/fɪlm/	
flashlight (n)	/ˈflæʃlaɪt/	
flat (n)	/flæt/	
fold your arms (v)	/fəʊld jɔː(r) ɑːmz/	
friendliness (n)	/ˈfrendlinəs/	
frown (v)	/fraʊn/	
gasp (v)	/gɑːsp/	
give a thumbs up (v)	/gɪv ə θʌmz ʌp/	
give presents (v)	/gɪv ˈpreznts/	
grimace (v)	/ˈgrɪməs/	
grin (v)	/grɪn/	
happiness (n)	/ˈhæpinəs/	
harelipped (adj) (Old-fashioned – now considered offensive. The accepted medical term is *cleft lip* /kleft lɪp/)	/heə lɪpt/	
hiccup (v)	/ˈhɪkʌp/	
highway (n)	/ˈhaɪweɪ/	
ignorance (n)	/ˈɪgnərəns/	
indifference (n)	/ɪnˈdɪfrəns/	
interest (n)	/ˈɪntrəst/	
lift (n)	/lɪft/	

line (n)	/laɪn/	
longhaired (adj)	/lɒŋ ˈheəd/	
low-set (adj)	/ləʊ set/	
mobile (n)	/ˈməʊbaɪl/	
motorway (n)	/ˈməʊtəweɪ/	
nod your head (v)	/nɒd jɔː hed/	
pain (n)	/peɪn/	
pavement (n)	/ˈpeɪvmənt/	
petrol (n)	/ˈpetrəl/	
point (v)	/pɔɪnt/	
pout (v)	/paʊt/	
prepare (a meal) (v)	/prɪˈpeə/	
public holiday (n)	/ˌpʌblɪk ˈhɒlədeɪ/	
purse your lips (v)	/pɜːs jɔː lɪps/	
queue (n)	/kjuː/	
raise your eyebrows (v)	/reɪz jɔː(r) ˈaɪbraʊz/	
scowl (v)	/skaʊl/	
scratch your head (v)	/skrætʃ jɔː hed/	
shake your head (v)	/ʃeɪk jɔː hed/	
shame (n)	/ʃeɪm/	
shock (n)	/ʃɒk/	
shrug your shoulders (v)	/ʃrʌg jɔː ˈʃəʊldəz/	
sidewalk (n)	/ˈsaɪdwɔːk/	
sigh (v)	/saɪ/	
slurp (v)	/slɜːp/	
sneakers (n)	/ˈsniːkəz/	
sneeze (v)	/sniːz/	
sniff (v)	/snɪf/	
snore (v)	/snɔː/	
souvenirs (n)	/ˌsuːvəˈnɪəz/	
special dishes (n)	/ˈspeʃl dɪʃɪz/	
special occasion (n)	/ˈspeʃl əˈkeɪʒn/	
surprise (n)	/səˈpraɪz/	
sweets (n)	/swiːts/	
tap (n)	/tæp/	
thin-boned (adj)	/θɪn bəʊnd/	
toilet (n)	/ˈtɔɪlət/	
torch (n)	/tɔːtʃ/	
traditional (meal/custom/ gift) (n)	/trəˈdɪʃənl/	
trainers (n)	/ˈtreɪnəz/	
tut (v)	/tʌt/	
wave (v)	/weɪv/	
wink (v)	/wɪŋk/	
yawn (v)	/jɔːn/	

Unit 4

adventure holiday (n)	/ədˈventʃə ˈhɒlədeɪ/	
B&B (n)	/ˌbiː ən ˈbiː/	
backpacking (n)	/ˈbækpækɪŋ/	
be physically active (v)	/bi ˈfɪzɪkli ˈæktɪv/	
beach holiday (n)	/biːtʃ ˈhɒlədeɪ/	
beach house (n)	/biːtʃ haʊs/	
boredom (n)	/ˈbɔːdəm/	
breathtaking (adj)	/ˈbreθteɪkɪŋ/	
broaden your horizons (v)	/ˈbrɔːdn jɔː həˈraɪznz/	
cabin (n)	/ˈkæbɪn/	
campervan (n)	/ˈkæmpə væn/	
camping (n)	/ˈkæmpɪŋ/	
campsite (n)	/ˈkæmpsaɪt/	
caravan (n)	/ˈkærəvæn/	
city break (n)	/ˈsɪti breɪk/	
closely	/ˈkləʊsli/	
come across (phr v)	/kʌm əˈkrɒs/	
comfort (n)	/ˈkʌmfət/	
commercialised (adj)	/kəˈmɜːʃəlaɪzd/	
convenience (n)	/kənˈviːniəns/	
cost (n)	/kɒst/	

cottage (n)	/ˈkɒtɪdʒ/	
couch-surfing (n)	/kaʊtʃ ˈsɜːfɪŋ/	
cruise (n)	/kruːz/	
cycling holiday (n)	/ˈsaɪklɪŋ ˈhɒlədeɪ/	
dingy (adj)	/ˈdɪndʒi/	
do some volunteer work (v)	/du səm ˌvɒlənˈtɪə wɜːk/	
dull (adj)	/dʌl/	
early	/ˈɜːli/	
eat out (v)	/iːt aʊt/	
ecotourism (n)	/ˈiːkəʊtʊərɪzəm/	
enjoy the nightlife (v)	/ɪnˈdʒɔɪ ðə ˈnaɪtlaɪf/	
fast	/fɑːst/	
find adventure (v)	/faɪnd ədˈventʃə/	
friendly	/ˈfrendli/	
get around (phr v)	/get əˈraʊnd/	
get away from it all (v)	/get əˈweɪ frɒm ɪt ɔːl/	
get back (phr v)	/get bæk/	
go off (phr v)	/gəʊ ɒf/	
go off the beaten track (v)	/gəʊ ɒf ðə ˈbiːtn træk/	
guest house (n)	/ˈgest haʊs/	
hang out with your friends (v)	/hæŋ aʊt wɪð jɔː frendz/	
have a lovely view (v)	/hæv ə ˈlʌvli vjuː/	
have new experiences (v)	/hæv njuː ɪkˈspɪəriənsɪz/	
help with your bags (v)	/help wɪð jɔː bægz/	
holiday camp (n)	/ˈhɒlədeɪ kæmp/	
holiday home (n)	/ˈhɒlədeɪ həʊm/	
hospitable (adj)	/hɒˈspɪtəbl/	
hotel (n)	/həʊˈtel/	
house swap (n)	/haʊs swɒp/	
houseboat (n)	/ˈhaʊsbəʊt/	
inaccessible (adj)	/ˌɪnækˈsesəbl/	
lately	/ˈleɪtli/	
light the campfire (v)	/laɪt ðə ˈkæmpfaɪə/	
luggage (n)	/ˈlʌgɪdʒ/	
meet people (v)	/miːt ˈpiːpl/	
mind-blowing (adj)	/ˈmaɪnd bləʊɪŋ/	
overcrowded (adj)	/ˌəʊvəˈkraʊdɪd/	
package holiday (n)	/ˈpækɪdʒ hɒlədeɪ/	
pamper yourself (v)	/ˈpæmpə jɔːˈself/	
pull up (phr v)	/ˈpʊl ʌp/	
put up the tent (v)	/pʊt ʌp ðə tent/	
recharge your batteries (v)	/ˌriːˈtʃɑːdʒ jɔː ˈbætəriz/	
remote (adj)	/rɪˈməʊt/	
run-down (adj)	/ˈrʌndaʊn/	
safety (n)	/ˈseɪfti/	
see the sights (v)	/siː ðə saɪts/	
self-catering apartment (n)	/self ˈkeɪtərɪŋ əˈpɑːtmənt/	
set off	/set ɒf/	
sleep rough (v)	/sliːp rʌf/	
stop over (phr v)	/ˈstɒpəʊvə/	
take in (phr v)	/teɪk ɪn/	
take it easy (v)	/teɪk ɪt ˈiːzi/	
taste a local dish (v)	/teɪst ə ˈləʊkl dɪʃ/	
tent (n)	/tent/	
time (n)	/taɪm/	
time-share apartment (n)	/taɪm ʃeə(r) əˈpɑːtmənt/	
travel light (v)	/ˈtrævl laɪt/	
travel sickness (n)	/ˈtrævl ˈsɪknəs/	
try local food (v)	/traɪ ˈləʊkl fuːd/	
unique (adj)	/juːˈniːk/	
unspoiled (adj)	/ˌʌnˈspɔɪld/	
vibrant (adj)	/ˈvaɪbrənt/	
villa (n)	/ˈvɪlə/	
volunteering (n)	/ˌvɒlənˈtɪərɪŋ/	
weekly	/ˈwiːkli/	
winter sports holiday (n)	/ˈwɪntə spɔːts ˈhɒlədeɪ/	
youth hostel (n)	/ˈjuːθ hɒstl/	

Wordlist

Unit 5

admire (v)	/əd'maɪə/	
adore (v)	/ə'dɔː/	
background (n)	/'bækgraʊnd/	
be (very) close (to) (v)	/bi 'kləʊs/	
be on the same wavelength (as) (v)	/bi ɒn ðə seɪm 'weɪvleŋθ æz/	
be wary of (v)	/bi 'weəri ɒv/	
compliment (sb on sth) (v)	/'kɒmplɪmənt/	
confirm (v)	/kən'fɜːm/	
despise (v)	/dɪ'spaɪz/	
envy (v)	/'envi/	
feel sorry for (v)	/fiːl 'sɒri fɔː/	
findings (n)	/'faɪndɪŋs/	
flatter (sb) (v)	/'flætə/	
gene (n)	/dʒiːn/	
guinea pig (n)	/'gɪni pɪg/	
have a lot in common (with) (v)	/həv ə lɒt ɪn 'kɒmən/	
have nothing in common (with) (v)	/həv 'nʌθɪŋ ɪn 'kɒmən/	
immune system (n)	/ɪ'mjuːn sɪstəm/	
in depth	/ɪn 'depθ/	
insult (sb) (v)	/ɪn'sʌlt/	
lecture (sb about sth) (v)	/'lektʃə/	
look down on (v)	/lʊk daʊn ɒn/	
look up to (v)	/lʊk ʌp tə/	
mate (n)	/meɪt/	
nag (sb about sth) (v)	/næg/	
not see eye to eye (with) (v)	/nɒt siː aɪ tə aɪ wɪð/	
offend (sb) (v)	/ə'fend/	
offspring (n)	/'ɒfsprɪŋ/	
organ (n)	/'ɔːgən/	
paper (n)	/'peɪpə/	
praise (sb for sth) (v)	/preɪz/	
proof (n)	/pruːf/	
release (v)	/rɪ'liːs/	
respect (v)	/rɪ'spekt/	
tease (sb about sth) (v)	/tiːz/	
tell (sb) off (for sth) (v)	/tel ɒf/	
trust (v)	/trʌst/	
warn (sb about sth) (v)	/wɔːn/	

Unit 6

absent-minded (adj)	/ˌæbsənt 'maɪndɪd/	
ache (v)	/eɪk/	
ache (n)	/eɪk/	
addictive (adj)	/ə'dɪktɪv/	
adrenalin (n)	/ə'drenəlɪn/	
antacid (n)	/ænt'æsɪd/	
antibiotics (n)	/ˌæntibaɪ'ɒtɪks/	
antihistamine (n)	/ˌænti'hɪstəmiːn/	
anti-inflammatories (n)	/ˈænti ɪn'flæmətriz/	
antiseptic cream (n)	/ˌænti'septɪk kriːm/	
attend a fitness class (v)	/ə'tend ə 'fɪtnəs klɑːs/	
badly paid (adj)	/'bædli peɪd/	
bandage (n)	/'bændɪdʒ/	
be competitive (v)	/bi kəm'petətɪv/	
beat an opponent (v)	/biːt æn ə'pəʊnənt/	
bruise (n)	/bruːz/	
burn (v)	/bɜːn/	
burst (n)	/bɜːst/	
calcium (n)	/'kælsiəm/	
calories (n)	/'kæləriz/	
carbohydrate (n)	/ˌkɑːbəʊ'haɪdreɪt/	
cheap (adj)	/tʃiːp/	

chest infection (n)	/tʃest ɪn'fekʃn/	
cholesterol (n)	/kə'lestərɒl/	
(be) congested (adj)	/kən'dʒestɪd/	
convenient (adj)	/kən'viːniənt/	
convert (v)	/kən'vɜːt/	
cough (n)	/kɒf/	
cough medicine (n)	/kɒf 'medɪsn/	
cut (n)	/kʌt/	
dairy products (n)	/'deəri 'prɒdʌkts/	
densely populated (adj)	/densli 'pɒpjuleɪtɪd/	
(feel) dizzy (adj)	/'dɪzi/	
do aerobics (v)	/du eə'rəʊbɪks/	
energy (n)	/'enədʒi/	
English-speaking (adj)	/'ɪŋglɪʃ -spiːkɪŋ/	
expensive (adj)	/ɪk'spensɪv/	
far-reaching (adj)	/ˌfɑː 'riːtʃɪŋ/	
fat (n)	/fæt/	
(feel) fatigued (adj)	/fə'tiːgd/	
fever (n)	/'fiːvə/	
fibre (n)	/'faɪbə/	
flu (n)	/fluː/	
fracture (n)	/'fræktʃə/	
free choice (n)	/friː tʃɔɪs/	
fresh (adj)	/freʃ/	
go running (v)	/gəʊ 'rʌnɪŋ/	
heartburn (n)	/'hɑːtbɜːn/	
high-calorie (adj)	/haɪ 'kæləri/	
highly paid (adj)	/'haɪli peɪd/	
ingredient (n)	/ɪn'griːdiənt/	
insect sting (n)	/'ɪnsekt stɪŋ/	
intensity (n)	/ɪn'tensəti/	
keep fit (v)	/kiːp fɪt/	
lift weights (v)	/lɪft weɪts/	
light-hearted (adj)	/ˌlaɪt 'hɑːtɪd/	
lots of liquids (n)	/lɒts ɒv 'lɪkwɪdz/	
low-calorie (adj)	/ləʊ 'kæləri/	
mineral (n)	/'mɪnərəl/	
mouth-watering (adj)	/'maʊθ wɔːtərɪŋ/	
much-needed (adj)	/mʌtʃ niːdɪd/	
(feel) nauseous (adj)	/'nɔːziəs/	
nose bleed (n)	/'nəʊzbliːd/	
nutrient (n)	/'njuːtriənt/	
nuts (n)	/nʌts/	
oil (n)	/ɔɪl/	
old-fashioned (adj)	/ˌəʊld 'fæʃənd/	
painkillers (n)	/'peɪnkɪləz/	
pedal on a bike (v)	/'pedl ɒn ə baɪk/	
penicillin (n)	/ˌpenɪ'sɪlɪn/	
play a team sport (v)	/pleɪ ə tiːm spɔːt/	
poultry (n)	/'pəʊltri/	
preservative (n)	/prɪ'zɜːvətɪv/	
processed (adj)	/'prəʊsest/	
processed food (n)	/'prəʊsest fuːd/	
processed meat (n)	/'prəʊsest miːt/	
protein (n)	/'prəʊtiːn/	
pump (v)	/pʌmp/	
push myself to the limit (v)	/pʊʃ maɪ'self tə ðə 'lɪmɪt/	
rash (n)	/ræʃ/	
record-breaking (adj)	/'rekɔːd breɪkɪŋ/	
rest (n)	/rest/	
salt (n)	/sɒlt/	
seeds (n)	/siːdz/	
sore throat (n)	/sɔː θrəʊt/	
sprain (n)	/spreɪn/	
(feel) stiff (adj)	/stɪf/	
sugar (n)	/'ʃʊgə/	
(be) swollen (adj)	/'swəʊlən/	
tablets (n)	/'tæbləts/	

tasty (adj)	/ˈteɪsti/
temperature (n)	/ˈtemprətʃə/
throat sweets (n)	/θrəʊt swiːts/
time-saving (adj)	/taɪm ˈseɪvɪŋ/
value for money (adj)	/ˈvæljuː fə ˈmʌni/
virus (n)	/ˈvaɪrəs/
vitamins (n)	/ˈvɪtəmɪnz/
well-respected (adj)	/wel rɪˈspektɪd/
well-written (adj)	/wel ˈrɪtn/
wholegrain (n)	/ˈhəʊlɡreɪn/
will power (n)	/ˈwɪlpaʊə/
wound (n)	/wuːnd/
X-ray (n)	/ˈeks reɪ/

Unit 7

addiction (to) (n)	/əˈdɪkʃn/
admit (v)	/ədˈmɪt/
angry (adj)	/ˈæŋɡri/
announce (v)	/əˈnaʊns/
belief (in) (n)	/bɪˈliːf/
biased (adj)	/ˈbaɪəst/
cheat (v)	/tʃiːt/
control (over) (n)	/kənˈtrəʊl/
deceive sb (v)	/dɪˈsiːv ˈsʌmbədi/
demand (for) (n)	/dɪˈmɑːnd/
deny (v)	/dɪˈnaɪ/
dependence (on) (n)	/dɪˈpendəns/
difference (between) (n)	/ˈdɪfrəns/
direct (adj)	/daɪˈrekt/
disguise (the truth, the fact that, etc.) (v)	/dɪsˈɡaɪz/
dishonest (adj)	/dɪsˈɒnɪst/
effect (on) (n)	/ɪˈfekt/
enthusiastic (adj)	/ɪnˌθjuːziˈæstɪk/
ethical (adj)	/ˈeθɪkl/
evidence (of) (n)	/ˈevɪdəns/
exaggerate (v)	/ɪɡˈzædʒəreɪt/
exaggerate (the truth, a difficulty, etc.) (v)	/ɪɡˈzædʒəreɪt/
existence (of) (n)	/ɪɡˈzɪstəns/
explain (v)	/ɪkˈspleɪn/
fabricate (a story, evidence, etc.) (v)	/ˈfæbrɪkeɪt/
fib (v)	/fɪb/
find out (phr v)	/faɪnd aʊt/
fool sb (v)	/fuːl ˈsʌmbədi/
hole up (phr v)	/həʊl ʌp/
honest (adj)	/ˈɒnɪst/
hypocritical (adj)	/ˌhɪpəˈkrɪtɪkl/
increase (in) (n)	/ˈɪŋkriːs/
insist (v)	/ɪnˈsɪst/
interest (in) (n)	/ˈɪntrəst/
let on (phr v)	/let ɒn/
lie (about sth / to sb) (v)	/laɪ/
make an excuse (v)	/meɪk ən ɪkˈskjuːs/
make out (phr v)	/meɪk aʊt/
manipulate (sb) (v)	/məˈnɪpjuleɪt ˈsʌmbədi/
manipulative (adj)	/məˈnɪpjələtɪv/
mislead sb (v)	/ˌmɪsˈliːd ˈsʌmbədi/
need (for) (n)	/niːd/
nervous (adj)	/ˈnɜːvəs/
objection (to) (n)	/əbˈdʒekʃn/
obsession (with) (n)	/əbˈseʃn/
open (adj)	/ˈəʊpən/
own up (to sth) (v)	/əʊn ʌp/
pass sth/sb off as (v)	/pɑːs ˈsʌmθɪŋ / ˈsʌmbədi ɒf æz/
patient (adj)	/ˈpeɪʃnt/

photoshop (a picture, an image, etc.) (v)	/ˈfəʊtəʊʃɒp/
play on (phr v)	/pleɪ ɒn/
preference (for) (n)	/ˈprefrəns/
promise (v)	/ˈprɒmɪs/
reason (for) (n)	/ˈriːzn/
reveal (a secret, the truth, etc.) (v)	/rɪˈviːl/
rise (in) (n)	/raɪz/
sarcastic (adj)	/sɑːˈkæstɪk/
set up (phr v)	/ˌset ˈʌp/
solution (to) (n)	/səˈluːʃn/
surprised (adj)	/səˈpraɪzd/
swear that / to do sth (v)	/sweə ðæt / tə duː ˈsʌmθɪŋ/
take in (phr v)	/teɪk ɪn/
tell a lie (v)	/tel ə laɪ/
tell the truth (v)	/tel ðə truːθ/
zoom in on (phr v)	/zuːm ɪn ɒn/

Unit 8

arrest (v)	/əˈrest/
ban (v)	/bæn/
campaign against (v)	/kæmˈpeɪn əˈɡeɪnst/
censorship (n)	/ˈsensəʃɪp/
corruption (n)	/kəˈrʌpʃn/
decide (v)	/dɪˈsaɪd/
demonstrate (v)	/ˈdemənstreɪt/
demonstrate/protest against (sth) (v)	/ˈdemənstreɪt / ˈprəʊtest əˈɡeɪnst/
disease (n)	/dɪˈziːz/
famine (n)	/ˈfæmɪn/
gang (n)	/ɡæŋ/
gender inequality (n)	/ˈdʒendə(r) ˌɪnɪˈkwɒləti/
get ahead (phr v)	/ɡet əˈhed/
global warming (n)	/ˌɡləʊbl ˈwɔːmɪŋ/
globalisation (n)	/ˌɡləʊbəlaɪˈzeɪʃn/
go on a demonstration/a march (v)	/ɡəʊ ɒn ə ˌdemənˈstreɪʃn / ə mɑːtʃ/
help out (phr v)	/help aʊt/
hide (v)	/haɪd/
hold a rally (v)	/həʊld ə ˈræli/
hold up placards (v)	/həʊld ʌp ˈplækɑːdz/
homelessness (n)	/ˈhəʊmləsnəs/
immigration (n)	/ˌɪmɪˈɡreɪʃn/
investigate (v)	/ɪnˈvestɪɡeɪt/
keep (v)	/kiːp/
listen to speeches (v)	/ˈlɪsn tə ˈspiːtʃɪz/
misunderstood (adj)	/ˌmɪsʌndəˈstʊd/
nuclear weapons (n)	/ˈnjuːkliə ˈwepənz/
organise a protest (v)	/ˈɔːɡənaɪz ə ˈprəʊtest/
put in (phr v)	/pʊt ɪn/
racism (n)	/ˈreɪsɪzəm/
resign (v)	/rɪˈzaɪn/
set up (phr v)	/ˌset ˈʌp/
shout slogans (v)	/ʃaʊt ˈsləʊɡənz/
sign (v)	/saɪn/
sign a petition (v)	/saɪn ə pəˈtɪʃn/
social conscience (n)	/ˌsəʊʃl ˈkɒnʃəns/
squeeze in (phr v)	/skwiːz ɪn/
stand for election (v)	/stænd fɔː(r) ɪˈlekʃn/
step down (phr v)	/step daʊn/
support a campaign (v)	/səˈpɔːt ə kæmˈpeɪn/
take on (phr v)	/teɪk ɒn/
tell (v)	/tel/
terrorism (n)	/ˈterərɪzəm/
think up (phr v)	/θɪŋk ʌp/
thoughtful (adj)	/ˈθɔːtfl/

Wordlist

thoughtless (adj)	/ˈθɔːtləs/	_____
threatening (adj)	/ˈθretnɪŋ/	_____
throw (v)	/θrəʊ/	_____
unemployment (n)	/ˌʌnɪmˈplɔɪmənt/	_____
vandalism (n)	/ˈvændəlɪzəm/	_____
volunteer (n)	/ˌvɒlənˈtɪə/	_____
vote in elections (v)	/vəʊt ɪn ɪˈlekʃns/	_____
wait (v)	/weɪt/	_____
wonder (v)	/ˈwʌndə/	_____
write to a politician (v)	/raɪt tuː ə ˌpɒləˈtɪʃn/	_____

Unit 9

afford (v)	/əˈfɔːd/	_____
basket (n)	/ˈbɑːskɪt/	_____
be a rip-off	/bi ə rɪp ɒf/	_____
be broke	/bi brəʊk/	_____
be dirt cheap	/bi dɜːt tʃiːp/	_____
be hard up	/bi hɑːd ʌp/	_____
be rolling in it	/bi ˈrəʊlɪŋ ɪn ɪt/	_____
be well off	/bi wel ɒf/	_____
brand (n)	/brænd/	_____
budget (v)	/ˈbʌdʒɪt/	_____
burglar (n)	/ˈbɜːglə/	_____
burglary (n)	/ˈbɜːgləri/	_____
burgle (v)	/ˈbɜːgl/	_____
check out (phr v)	/ˈtʃek aʊt/	_____
checkout (n)	/ˈtʃekaʊt/	_____
commercial (n)	/kəˈmɜːʃl/	_____
consumer (n)	/kənˈsjuːmə/	_____
delivery (n)	/dɪˈlɪvəri/	_____
endorsement (n)	/ɪnˈdɔːsmənt/	_____
fork out (v)	/fɔːk aʊt/	_____
get into debt (phr v)	/get ˈɪntə det/	_____
haggle (v)	/ˈhægl/	_____
item (n)	/ˈaɪtəm/	_____
jingle (n)	/ˈdʒɪŋgl/	_____
knock down (phr v)	/ˈnɒk daʊn/	_____
launch (n)	/lɔːntʃ/	_____
logo (n)	/ˈləʊgəʊ/	_____
notification (n)	/ˌnəʊtɪfɪˈkeɪʃn/	_____
overcharge (v)	/ˌəʊvəˈtʃɑːdʒ/	_____
overspend (v)	/ˌəʊvəˈspend/	_____
pick up a bargain (v)	/ˈpɪk ʌp ə ˈbɑːgɪn/	_____
review (n)	/rɪˈvjuː/	_____
rip off (phr v)	/rɪp ˈɒf/	_____
rob (v)	/rɒb/	_____
robber (n)	/ˈrɒbə/	_____
robbery (n)	/ˈrɒbəri/	_____
scan (v)	/skæn/	_____
shop around (phr v)	/ʃɒp əˈraʊnd/	_____
shoplift (v)	/ˈʃɒplɪft/	_____
shoplifter (n)	/ˈʃɒplɪftə/	_____
shoplifting (n)	/ˈʃɒplɪftɪŋ/	_____
slogan (n)	/ˈsləʊgən/	_____
snap up (phr v)	/snæp ʌp/	_____
splash out (phr v)	/splæʃ aʊt/	_____
steal (v)	/stiːl/	_____
theft (n)	/θeft/	_____
thief (n)	/θiːf/	_____
track (v)	/træk/	_____
vandal (n)	/ˈvændl/	_____
vandalise (v)	/ˈvændəlaɪz/	_____
vandalism (n)	/ˈvændəlɪzəm/	_____
wishlist (n)	/ˈwɪʃlɪst/	_____

I Irregular verbs

Base form	Past simple	Past participle
be	was / were	been
become	became	become
begin	began	begun
bend	bent	bent
bite	bit	bitten
blow	blew	blown
break	broke	broken
bring	brought	brought
build	built	built
burn	burned / burnt	burned / burnt
buy	bought	bought

Base form	Past simple	Past participle
can	could	been able to
catch	caught	caught
choose	chose	chosen
come	came	come
cost	cost	cost
cut	cut	cut

Base form	Past simple	Past participle
do	did	done
draw	drew	drawn
drink	drank	drunk
drive	drove	driven

Base form	Past simple	Past participle
eat	ate	eaten

Base form	Past simple	Past participle
fall	fell	fallen
feel	felt	felt
fight	fought	fought
find	found	found
fly	flew	flown
forget	forgot	forgotten

Base form	Past simple	Past participle
get	got	got
give	gave	given
go	went	gone
grow	grew	grown

Base form	Past simple	Past participle
hang	hung	hung
have	had	had
hear	heard	heard
hide	hid	hidden
hit	hit	hit

Base form	Past simple	Past participle
keep	kept	kept
know	knew	known

Base form	Past simple	Past participle
lay	laid	laid
lead	led	led
learn	learned / learnt	learned / learnt
leave	left	left

Base form	Past simple	Past participle
lend	lent	lent
lose	lost	lost

Base form	Past simple	Past participle
make	made	made
mean	meant	meant
meet	met	met

Base form	Past simple	Past participle
overcome	overcame	overcome

Base form	Past simple	Past participle
pay	paid	paid
put	put	put

Base form	Past simple	Past participle
read	read	read
ride	rode	ridden
ring	rang	rung
run	ran	run

Base form	Past simple	Past participle
say	said	said
see	saw	seen
sell	sold	sold
send	sent	sent
set	set	set
shake	shook	shaken
shine	shone	shone
shoot	shot	shot
show	showed	shown / showed
shut	shut	shut
sing	sang	sung
sink	sank	sunk
sit	sat	sat
sleep	slept	slept
smell	smelled / smelt	smelled / smelt
speak	spoke	spoken
spell	spelled / spelt	spelled / spelt
spend	spent	spent
spill	spilled / spilt	spilled / spilt
stand	stood	stood
steal	stole	stolen
swim	swam	swum

Base form	Past simple	Past participle
take	took	taken
teach	taught	taught
tell	told	told
think	thought	thought
throw	threw	thrown

Base form	Past simple	Past participle
understand	understood	understood

Base form	Past simple	Past participle
wake	woke	woken
wear	wore	worn
win	won	won
write	wrote	written